D1072175

EFFECTIVE USE
OF THE SEA

REPORT OF THE PANEL ON OCEANOGRAPHY
PRESIDENT'S SCIENCE ADVISORY COMMITTEE

THE WHITE HOUSE
JUNE 1966

DUQUESNE UNIVERSITY LIBRARY
PITTSBURGH, PA. 15219

- 35.8 . See 2 feet

EFFECTIVE USE
OF THE SEA

REPORT OF THE PANEL ON OCEANOGRAPHY

OF THE

PRESIDENT'S SCIENCE ADVISORY COMMITTEE

U.S. President's Science
Advisory Committee.
Panel on Oceanographic.

JUNE 1966

For sale by the Superintendent of Documents, U.S. Government Printing Office
Washington, D.C., 20402 - Price 60 cents

551.46

U58

June 17, 1966

Nature has lavished incredible bounty on this earth. Warmed
daily by the sun, nourished by the land, sustained by atmosphere
and water, man takes these riches largely for granted and often
complains when they fail to suit his convenience exactly. But
man can also use his energies and talents, constructively, to
improve his surroundings.

Much of our natural bounty consists of water. A source of fish
and transport to the ancients, as they are today, the oceans of
the world hold great promise to provide future generations with
minerals, food, energy, and fresh water. We must turn our
attention to finding more appropriate ways and better means of
transforming this promise into achievement.

This comprehensive report presents the findings and conclusions
of a group of outstanding men who are deeply concerned to learn
more about the oceans and how they can be made to serve mankind.
I commend it to all who share that concern and ask the appropriate
agencies and councils of the Federal Government to consider its
recommendations.

GC 58
.A57

II

PRESIDENT'S SCIENCE ADVISORY COMMITTEE

Chairman

DR. DONALD F. HORNIG
Special Assistant to the President for Science and Technology

Vice Chairman

DR. HERBERT F. YORK, JR.
Professor of Physics
University of California, San Diego

DR. IVAN L. BENNETT, JR.
Johns Hopkins Hospital

DR. LEWIS M. BRANSCOMB
Chairman
Joint Institute for Laboratory Astrophysics

DR. MELVIN CALVIN
Professor of Chemistry
University of California, Berkeley

DR. SIDNEY D. DRELL
Stanford Linear Accelerator Center

DR. MARVIN L. GOLDBERGER
Professor of Physics
Palmer Physical Laboratory
Princeton University

DR. PHILIP HANDLER
Chairman
Department of Biochemistry
Duke University Medical Center

MR. WILLIAM R. HEWLETT
President
Hewlett-Packard Company

DR. FRANKLIN A. LONG
Vice President for Research and Advanced Studies
Cornell University

DR. GORDON J. F. MACDONALD
Chairman, Department of Planetary and Space Physics
Institute of Geophysics and Planetary Physics
University of California, Los Angeles

DR. WILLIAM D. McELROY
Chairman
Department of Biology
The Johns Hopkins University

DR. GEORGE E. PAKE
Provost
Washington University

DR. JOHN R. PIERCE
Executive Director, Research
Communications Sciences Division
Bell Telephone Laboratories

DR. KENNETH S. PITZER
President
Rice University

DR. FREDERICK SEITZ
President
National Academy of Sciences

Dr. CHARLES P. SLICHTER
Department of Physics
University of Illinois

DR. CHARLES H. TOWNES
Provost
Massachusetts Institute of Technology

MAR 3 1971

Contents

SUMMARY OF MAJOR FINDINGS AND RECOMMEN- Page
DATIONS _____ IX

Introduction _____ IX
Findings and Recommendations _____ X

1.0 INTRODUCTION _____ 1

   1.1 Goals for a National Ocean Program _____ 1
   1.2 Panel Objectives and Organization _____ 3

2.0 FOOD FROM THE SEA _____ 5

   2.1 Introduction _____ 5
   2.2 Protein Production in the Sea _____ 7
   2.3 The World Fish Catch _____ 7
   2.4 Utilization of Fish for Human Consumption _____ 9
   2.5 Aquiculture _____ 10
   2.6 Summary _____ 15

3.0 MODIFICATION OF THE OCEAN ENVIRONMENT _ 16

   3.1 Introduction _____ 16
   3.2 General Considerations _____ 16
   3.3 Specific Considerations _____ 17
   3.4 What Needs To Be Done _____ 18
   3.5 Summary _____ 19

4.0 UNDERSEA TECHNOLOGY _____ 20

   4.1 Materials _____ 21
   4.2 Instruments and Tools _____ 21
   4.3 Positioning Problems _____ 21
   4.4 Identification of Objects _____ 22
   4.5 Tools Problem _____ 22
   4.6 Services _____ 23
   4.7 Standards _____ 24
   4.8 Surf Zone and Beach Engineering Problems _____ 25
   4.9 Buoys _____ 26
   4.10 New Lightweight, Compact Power Plant _____ 26
   4.11 Man in the Sea _____ 27
   4.12 Marine Min'ng _____ 28

5.0 OCEAN SCIENCE AND TECHNOLOGY AND NATIONAL SECURITY ..... Page 30

5.1 Introduction 30
5.2 Vital Navy Missions Heavily Depende: t o . Ocean Science and Technology 30
5.3 The Navy's Oceanographic Program 34
5.4 The Navy's Role in Education and Research 37
5.5 Interaction of Navy Programs With Civilian Technology 39
5.6 Conclusions 39

6.0 OPPORTUNITIES IN OCEANOGRAPHIC RESEARCH 41

6.1 Observation 41
6.2 Prediction 42
6.3 Physical Processes 44
6.4 Biological Processes 49

7.0 ECONOMIC ASPECTS OF OCEANOGRAPHY 55
7.1 Introduction 55
7.2 An Economic Evaluation of the Oceanographic Program 57

8.0 CURRENT STATUS 66

8.1 Organizational Structure 66
8.2 Support 67
8.3 Manpower Considerations 70
8.4 National Interest in the Oceans 73

9.0 EDUCATION AND MANPOWER 76

9.1 General Requirements in Oceanographic Manpower 76
9.2 Education for Research Workers 76
9.3 Education for Technology and Commerce 78
9.4 Implications of Manpower Change 78
9.5 Marine Study Centers 79

10.0 FEDERAL ORGANIZATION AND PROGRAM 80

10.1 Federal Interest—Past and Present 80
10.2 Federal Role in a National Ocean Program 81
10.3 Present Organizational Structure 82
10.4 Organization for the Future 87
10.5 Legal Problems 91
10.6 Support and Operation of Oceanographic Ships 95
10.7 National Facilities 97

		Page
11.0 PRIORITIES		102
11.1	Ocean Science and Technology	102
11.2	Ocean Science and Technology in Comparison with Other Fields	104

APPENDIXES

I.	Panel Membership and Activities	106
II.	Moored-Buoy Array Program	112
III.	Industry and the Ocean Continental Shelf	119
	1. Introduction	119
	2. Recommendations	120
	3. Participants in Continental-Shelf Conference at David Taylor Model Basin	122
	4. Summary Findings of the Five Industries	125
	5. References	127
IV.	The National Oceanographic Program—A Perspective	128
V.	Earlier Views on Federal Reorganizations of the Environmental Sciences	134
VI.	Marine Resources and Engineering Development Act of 1966	136

SUBJECT INDEX	141

Summary of Major Findings and Recommendations

INTRODUCTION

The PSAC Panel on Oceanography was formed in May 1965 at a time when widespread and intense controversy existed concerning the adequacy of our national effort to explore, understand and develop the oceans. The controversy was illustrated by congressional hearings held in the summer of 1965 on some 19 bills submitted during the first session of the 89th Congress and by the formation of special industrial groups to examine oceanography. The Panel completed its report in June 1966 just as enactment of the Marine Resources and Engineering Development Act of 1966 assured the encouragements of a comprehensive and continuing long-range national program for the effective use of the sea.

Oceanography is defined in various ways depending on the concern of the definer. The Panel has adopted the broad view, prevalent in the Congress and industry, that oceanography connotes more than scientific study of the sea. In this report oceanography refers to *activities within the ocean that have significant scientific or technological content.*

In its studies the Panel had four principal objectives:

1. To draft a statement of goals for a national program to serve the marine interests of the United States and to define the Federal role in pursuit of these goals.

2. To assess current and planned ocean-oriented programs for technical soundness, adequacy of scope, balance of content, appropriateness of organization, funding, and management in light of relevant national goals.

3. To identify major opportunities for new programs in technology and science that should be given high priority in the next 5 to 10 years.

4. To recommend measures to effect an ocean science and technology program consonant with national needs and interests.

FINDINGS AND RECOMMENDATIONS

National Goals. The oceans' importance to national security, considered in the widest possible sense, requires that goals for the Nation's ocean program be clearly stated and that the program be oriented toward meeting these goals. The Panel therefore *recommends* that the President state the ultimate objective of the national ocean program as being *effective use of the sea by man for all purposes currently considered for the terrestrial environment: commerce; industry, recreation and settlement; as well as for knowledge and understanding.* This objective implies four specific goals:

1. Acquiring the ability to predict and ultimately control phenomena affecting the safety and economy of seagoing activities.

2. Undertaking measures required for fullest exploitation of resources represented by, in and under the sea.

3. Utilizing the sea to enhance national security.

4. Pursuing scientific investigations for describing and understanding marine phenomena, processes and resources (see sec. 1.1).

Role of the Federal Government. Great concern was evident within the private sector as to the Federal Government's proper role in developing the nation's ocean program. The Panel believes that division of effort among government, industry, and universities appropriate to land-based activities is advisable for the oceans and that the Federal Government should not preempt these activities to the extent it has, for example, in space. We *recommend* that the Government perform four functions in achieving the goals of the national ocean program:

1. Enunciate national policies concerning the marine interests of the United States.

2. Foster exploration, development and use of oceans and their resources through establishment of appropriate financial, legal, regulatory, enforcement and advisory institutions and measures.

3. Promote description and prediction of the marine environment and development of capabilities for its modification.

4. Initiate, support, and encourage programs of education, training, and research and provide technical services and facilities related to activities in pertinent sciences and technology (see sec. 10.2).

These Federal functions are not new; however, only the last two functions are to any degree developed and coordinated across existing agency lines. Systematic development and application by a more centralized authority are required for efficient implementation of the first two functions.

Oceans and National Security. Increased Federal participation in ocean activities is required for national security. The developing strategic situation, which may require a much improved undersea deterrent force, coupled with the need for defenses against missile-launching submarines, implies that the Navy must develop the capability to operate anywhere within the oceans at any time. The Navy has underway a Deep Submergence Systems Project. This effort as presently constituted is insufficient if the Navy is to meet its goals in a reasonable time period. The Panel therefore *recommends* expansion of activities which will permit operation at any location and time within the oceans (see secs. 5.2, 5.3). It is *recommended* that a continuing, special effort be made by the Navy to utilize personnel, facilities and know-how of the private sector in achieving its objectives in the Deep Submergence Systems and Man in the Sea Projects (see secs. 4.11, 5.3). Navy technological results in these programs should be made available to industry upon acquisition.

The Navy presently has primary responsibility for development of capability for using man at depths in the oceans. The general level of research in the Man in the Sea Project is inadequate. Insufficient attention has been give to biomedical problems of survival in the wet, cold, dark, high-pressure environment, and our efforts in this field lag well behind those of other countries. If the goals of the Man in the Sea Project are to be achieved, adequate opportunities must be provided for basic studies by a variety of institutions. In particular we *recommend* establishment of a major shore facility fully equipped for the range of basic studies required by Man in the Sea. This facility should be associated with a university or medical research center. Navy efforts may need to be complemented through instrumented, movable, submersible laboratories for basic studies on man living beneath the sea's surface for extended periods. These laboratories should be available to a wide community of scholars outside the Navy who are interested in biomedical problems of man in the deep sea (see secs. 4.11, 10.7).

The Panel recognizes that development of adequate programs in undersea technology and Man in the Sea may be hampered by traditional views within the Navy to the effect that the Navy is primarily an *operating* force at or near the *surface*. If the Navy does not adequately pursue programs recommended in this report (see sec. 4), program responsibilities for Man in the Sea and undersea technology should be shifted to a civilian agency (see secs. 4, 5, 10.4).

The *Thresher* experience in 1963 and the recent lost nuclear weapon incident off the Spanish coast clearly illustrate the continuing importance of search-and-recovery capabilities. We *recommend* that ocean search-and-recovery missions related in any way to national security be the Navy's responsibility. However, the technology developed through such programs should be made available to industry on a current basis (see sec. 5.2).

The Navy should have broad responsibilities in furthering ocean science and technology in addition to its problem-oriented research. Most of the technology developed for undersea operations within the Government will result from the Navy's efforts. An important need is development of a test range equipped with standardized stations at which components, systems, concepts, and materials can be critically tested. Such a range will be an expensive undertaking, though of great value to private industry and university research. We therefore *recommend* that a supporting role of the Navy should be provision of test facilities that are open to scientific and technological communities. Users would be expected to pay a prorated share of operating costs and depreciation, as is the case in other national facilities (see secs. 4.7, 5.5).

The Navy has maintained good relations with the academic oceanographic community, and, in turn, the community has frequently responded to the Navy's needs in rapid and effective manner. The successful bomb recovery operations off the Spanish coast are a recent, dramatic but typical example of this cooperation. Long-term support of academic oceanography through the ONR has been fruitful in the past, and we *recommend* that the Navy continue these programs (see sec. 5.4). The total Navy commitment to ocean science and technology has almost doubled in fiscal year 1965–67, yet Navy support of basic research has remained constant. This situation cannot continue if the Navy is to make adequate use of new developments in ocean science and technology; therefore, the Panel *recommends* that Navy support of basic research in the oceans increase at a rate consonant with the total Navy program in ocean science and technology (see sec. 5.4).

Marine Food Resources. In the civilian sector economic analyses—admittedly crude because of lack of adequate data and previous analyses—suggest that activities related to improved weather prediction and the near-shore environment can be justified on economic grounds (see sec. 7.2). No similar *economic* justification for development of marine food resources exists; however, the Panel *recommends* that development of marine food resources be given very high priority for other vitally important reasons (see secs. 2.2, 2.4, 11.1).

A great public health problem is protein deficiency (it is the leading cause of death in the period between weaning and 5 years of age in certain countries). Proper long-range development of marine food resources requires numerous studies in marine biology. The protein-deficiency problem is so acute that efforts should be made to bypass the requirement for detailed understanding of means to obtain more food from the sea. New advances in development of marine food can greatly alleviate this problem, and we *recommend* expansion and improvement in technology for developing these resources and Government approval for human use of marine protein concentrate (see sec. 2.4).

Emphasis should be placed on development of this technology for export to underdeveloped countries in which malnutrition exists.

A program for the development of marine food resources offers a major opportunity for substantive international cooperation. Several countries, including Japan, U.S.S.R., and Norway, have advanced technologies for fishing. An international effort to further this technology and expand it to other marine food resources for the benefit of underdeveloped nations could be of major importance in achieving peace on earth. Such a program might be developed through auspices of the United Nations.

Preserving the Near-Shore Environment. Almost half our population lives near the margins of the oceans or the Great Lakes. The near-shore environment is thus of critical importance. This environment is being modified rapidly, by human activities, in ways that are unknown in detail but broadly are undesirable (see secs. 3, 6.4). Pollution, which renders beaches unsafe for swimmers, destroys valuable fisheries and generally degrades the coastline, is the chief modification. This problem is urgent, and dangers have not been adequately recognized. Specific recommendations cannot be made for solution of this serious problem because the research to date has been largely ineffectual. Therefore, the Panel *recommends* intensification of research in the area of pollution and pollution control.

Recommendations with regard to marine biology affect both the long-range goal of increasing marine food resources and preserving the near-shore environment. Specific *recommendations* are:

1. Intensive multidisciplinary studies of biological communities in marine habitats subject to human influence and exploitation. Such studies should include estuaries and the continental shelf. A very important, special case is the proposed sea level canal to join the Atlantic and Pacific Oceans (see secs. 3.3, 6.4).

2. Establishment of marine wilderness preserves to provide a baseline for future studies (see sec. 3.4).

3. Construction of facilities needed for studying organisms in special marine environments such as the deep sea and tropics (see sec. 10.7).

4. Increased encouragement and support of identification and use of marine organisms as tools for biomedical research and as potential sources of drugs (see sec. 6.4).

5. Establishment of a national center for collection, maintenance, and distribution of living marine organisms for use in marine and biological research (see sec. 10.7).

Unity of Environmental Sciences. Throughout its investigations the Panel has been impressed by the unity of environmental sciences. Methods of investigation, intellectual concepts and ways of analyzing data are remarkably alike in oceanography, meteorology and solid-earth geophysics. Educational, industrial, and governmental organizations for the most part have not taken advantage of this unity in developing their programs. The Panel's recommendations have been influenced to a large extent by similarities among these fields (see sec. 6).

Research in Oceanography. The Panel finds that much research effort in marine biology and physical oceanography during the last 10 years has concerned surveys of the ocean, measuring "classical" quantities. Such surveys were important 50 and even 20 years ago in defining problems; however, the subject has advanced to the stage that well-defined problems are *known* to exist. The Panel *recommends* that emphasis be shifted from *surveys* to *solutions* of these problems (see sec. 6). In section 6 a number of problems related to physical oceanography and marine biology are considered. A problem of great importance in physical oceanography both because of intrinsic scientific interest and possible contributions to security and commerce within the oceans is that of oceanic weather, weather being defined as fluctuations of temperature, pressure and current over a wide range of time and length scales. Major progress in this area can result from implementation of any of several buoy programs proposed heretofore. The Panel therefore *recommends* initiation of a step-by-step buoy program from detailed studies of limited regions to larger scale studies. A step-by-step program is necessary because buoy technology is not well developed (see secs. 6.3, 4.9, and app. II).

Development of undersea technology will depend on understanding the boundary between the oceans and the solid earth. Recent studies show that physical processes at this boundary are complex, and there is little understanding of them. The Panel *recommends* that high priority be given to benthic-boundary study (see sec. 6.3).

Education in Oceanography. Oceanographic education has been narrowly conceived and does not adequately recognize the importance of fundamental sciences in the subject's long-range development. The intellectual isolation of many oceanographic institutions needs to be corrected. Attempts should be made to associate oceanographic institutions with groups of universities to permit easy access by scientists and engineers throughout the country for work in ocean activities. The Panel questions the wisdom of granting Ph. D.'s in oceanography *per se* and feels education should be focused on a broad spectrum of environmental sciences, incorporating basic sciences. Many of the most active contributors to oceanography entered from other fields. This practice should be encouraged in the future, perhaps through special efforts in developing postdoctoral programs in oceanography (see secs. 9.1, 9.2, 9.3).

As activities in the oceans increase, it is clear that there will be interaction between those interested in the science and technology of the sea and those interested in legal, social, and economic aspects. We therefore *recommend* establishment and funding of Marine Study Centers to examine a wide range of problems associated with activities in the sea but not to be degree-granting organizations (see sec. 9.5). Research is particularly needed on economic aspects of ocean science and technology.

Ships for Oceanographic Research. A substantial portion of the personnel in numerous oceanographic institutions is concerned with administration and operation of ships. Ship time is more readily available to members of an institution than to scientists at universities and other organizations not directly connected with such an institution.

Within the institutions ship operations are no longer as flexible or as responsive to scientific objectives as they were 5 or 10 years ago. Operating costs of many ships are met by a conglomeration of grants and contracts. Because of administrative difficulties, we *recommend* comprehensive block-funding for oceanographic vessels (see sec. 10.6). The funding should imply a commitment for the operating cost of the ship for its expected life. Operating moneys should be funded separately from the oceanographic project for which the ship is used.

Block-funding will facilitate more effective planning and scheduling of oceanographic ships. It does not, however, solve the problem of access to ships by qualified scientists regardless of institutional affiliations. Therefore, we *recommend* that oceanographic ships be grouped generally into regional fleets of reasonable size. Perhaps three or four such fleets would serve the Nation's needs. Fleets should be assigned to independent regional organizations representing user groups from oceanographic laboratories and universities. Every effort should be made to include in user groups those institutions which at present do not have formal activity in ocean science and technology (see sec. 10.6).

Organization of Oceanography Within the Federal Government. No natural advocate for oceanography was found within the Federal establishment; responsibility for oceanography is diffused through a number of agencies. The Navy, of course, must maintain a strong oceanographic effort in order to meet its mission requirements. However, if the goal of effective use of the sea for all purposes now pursued on land is to be achieved, present methods of supporting civilian portions of the program are inadequate to the task, and basic revision of the system is necessary. In particular the Panel *recommends* that activities now included in the Environmental Science Services Administration, Geological Survey (regarding land and ocean activities), Bureau of Commercial Fisheries, oceanographic activities of the Bureau of Mines, and a portion of the oceanographic activities of the Coast Guard be combined in a single agency (see sec. 10.4). Such an agency would be competent to deal with the four governmental functions specified earlier. A reorganization of this type would recognize the fact that Federal activities related to description and prediction of the environment are very closely related, and one cannot sensibly separate the atmosphere from the oceans or the oceans from land. In addition, the ability to develop ocean resources and to use the oceans for commerce depends very heavily on our ability to describe and predict. There is thus an intimate connection between environmental sciences in providing services and development and use of ocean resources.

The Panel *recommends* that the Nation's oceanographic activities be supported in five ways:

1. By the NSF in its traditional role of supporting fundamental studies through grants and fellowships, with special emphasis on aspects that contribute to manpower education for ocean science and technology.

2. By the new agency in carrying out its responsibility for management of environment and ocean resources and for providing description and prediction services through a balanced program of direct participation and support of industry and universities.

3. By the Navy in discharging its mission of national security through its laboratories and industry and through ONR support of civilian institutions, as well as by its supporting role in the development of undersea technology and provision of national test facilities.

4. By agencies such as AEC and HEW in carrying out their missions.

5. By the Smithsonian Institution in fulfilling its major obligation to systematic biology (see sec. 10.4).

Creation of a mission-oriented agency, with major responsibilities as previously stated, does not by itself provide a clear mechanism for coordination, planning and budgeting. Several agencies, the Navy and NSF in particular, will continue to have major responsibilities in ocean-oriented activities. The need for information interchange and dissemination now discharged by ICO will continue, and we *recommend* formation of an interagency group under the Federal Council for Science and Technology to provide services now rendered by ICO and the Interagency Committee on Atmospheric Sciences (see sec. 10.4). This group should also have responsibilities for information interchange related to solid-earth sciences. It would thus link environmental science activities within the new agency to those in other agencies.

Budget allocations among the new agency, NSF, and the Navy would be made on a competitive basis, recognizing the mission responsibilities of the new agency and the Navy. The Federal Council, Bureau of the Budget, and Congress would all participate in the budgeting process. Although the proposed agency would not solve all problems of budgeting, it will provide a centralized authority with major mission responsibility.

Cost of Recommendations. We have not attempted to estimate costs of individual recommendations contained herein because more detailed studies will be required before such determinations can be made. Instead, we *recommend* a general increase of the nondefense component of the national oceanographic program from the present $120 million to $210 million by fiscal year 1971 (see sec. 7.2). This is based on foreseeable national needs for Federal services and support of marine science and technology. We do not propose a uniform expansion of the existing program; indeed, we believe some parts should be curtailed. We particularly *recommend* an increase in basic research and education support from about $15 million to at least $25 million by fiscal year 1971; these figures do not include cost of ships or other platforms.

The defense component of the oceanographic program will probably increase more than nondefense expenditures if these recommendations are implemented. The Navy needs large, expensive facilities for its program. Furthermore, we have charged it with construction and operation of facilities for other agencies, industry, and private research, and with continuing support of education and research. Under the circumstances a doubling of the present program by fiscal year 1971 would not be unexpected.

The total, therefore, would increase from $310 million in fiscal year 1967 to roughly $600 million in fiscal year 1971. Much of the nondefense increase would be devoted to economically promising programs or would support socially crucial ones.

1.0. Introduction

A number of reports have been written about the oceans and their vast resources. This report differs in that it views oceanography, broadly defined, as those activities in the ocean having significant scientific and technological content. The report is concerned with the marine activities of the Nation and how these activities contribute to the national well-being. Opportunities for the future are identified and discussed. However, the relative importance of these opportunities can be judged only when the national goals for the total ocean program are clearly defined.

1.1. GOALS FOR A NATIONAL OCEAN PROGRAM

Goals for a national ocean program must, of course, be based on marine interests of the United States. These interests are threefold: social, economic, and strategic. Science and technology supports these three concerns.

Marine science interests of the United States, which are shared by scientists around the world, involve observation, description and understanding of physical, chemical, and biological phenomena of the marine environment. Once adequately served by conventional oceanography, today marine science converges with meteorology and solid-earth geophysics so that consolidation into environmental science is required for progress in both research and education. This convergence is most advanced in programs aimed at environmental long-range prediction, modification, and control.

Similarly, technological—or engineering—needs of many environmental science programs are so extensive that the line between marine science and ocean engineering must be largely abolished, in practice if not in theory, if many important projects are to proceed effectively.

Marine economic interests of the United States entail shipping, food, minerals, and recreation. As on land, complex, interacting factors affect the profitability of efforts to exploit the seas' resources: access to markets, legal ownership of resources, availability of relevant technology and capital, strength of competition, safety of operations, and inadvertent or uncontrolled interference from other human activities such as waste disposal or warfare. Despite the many uncertainties,

1

developments detailed later in the report indicate that American industry may well be poised on the edge of what could, during the next 10 to 20 years, become a major, profitable advance into the marine environment.

Strategic marine interests of the United States have both military and nonmilitary aspects. Whereas the military aspect is both long standing and relatively familiar, the nonmilitary aspect is less well known and stems primarily from two developments of quite recent times:

1. The decreasing likelihood of a direct military confrontation between the United States and a highly industrialized nation such as Russia over territorial disputes, due to the unacceptable risk of mutual nuclear annihilation.

2. The increasing worldwide importance of more food, especially for underdeveloped nations, and the apparent possibility of a major breakdown of the world food economy within perhaps 20 years.

The first development strongly suggests that where competition develops for the acquisition of ocean resources such as fish, minerals, or even the right of passage, such nonmilitary factors as prior presence or continued use will in some contexts be decisive in determining the outcome.

The second development indicates a potential value that transcends mere monetary considerations of marine food resources for underdeveloped nations. Food from the sea offers at least temporary and local relief from exhausting efforts to feed increasing populations. The United States interest in these efforts is not only humanitarian, but is also national because of the worldwide political and social stability expected as a consequence. The strategic importance of food resources suggests a new focus for part of the national program.

These social, economic, and strategic marine interests interwoven and rapidly evolving in a context which includes similarly developing marine interests of other nations, seem to require establishment of a more comprehensive national program framework than is usually implied by the term, "oceanography," or is contemplated by any single, existing agency's missions. A truly adequate national ocean program should have as its ultimate objective *effective use of the sea* by man for all the purposes to which we now put the terrestrial environment: commerce, industry, recreation, and settlement, as well as for knowledge and understanding. This objective implies four specific goals:

1. Acquiring the ability to predict and ultimately to control phenomena affecting the safety and economy of seagoing activities.

2. Undertaking measures required for fullest exploitation of resources represented by, in and under the sea.

3. Employing the sea to enhance national security.

4. Pursuing scientific investigations for describing and understanding marine phenomena, processes and resources.

Effective human use of the sea does not imply any inevitable abridgment or infringement of other nations' rights or interests. In fact, the oceans are so huge and potential benefits so great that a cooperative, international effort to develop marine resources for the benefit of all humanity seems both logical and appealing. Institutional means for this development, however, are so rudimentary, and activities and interests of other nations are evolving so fast, that an *urgent* U.S. effort is required in the interim to preclude possible abridgment of *our* interests by others.

The implication is that "freedom of the seas" cannot be conceived as being static, especially since increasing intensity and sophistication of ocean exploitation require legal arrangements beyond the simple, traditional understanding of this concept. We do not wish to imply that more suitable versions of "freedom of the seas" must reflect narrow conceptions of *our* national interest. The problem is to adapt the principle of freedom to the *general* interest, rather than to any exclusive interest of our own. A realistic conception of freedom of the seas is likely to remain vital to protection of U.S. marine interests.

1.2. PANEL OBJECTIVES AND ORGANIZATION

The Panel adopted four main objectives:

1. To assess current and planned ocean programs for technical soundness, adequacy of scope, balance of content, adequacy of organization, and funding and management in light of relevant national goals.

2. To identify major opportunities for new programs in technology and science that should be given high priority in the next 5 to 10 years.

3. To draft a statement of goals designed to serve the marine interests of the United States and to define the Federal role in their pursuit.

4. To recommend measures to effect an ocean science and technology program consonant with national needs and interests.

Panel membership and a description of its activities are provided in appendix I. The Panel purposely reflects a diversity of backgrounds, experience and professional affiliations. The science of oceanography and related environmental sciences (meteorology and geophysics) are represented, as are biology, applied mathematics, physics, economics, and engineering. In terms of institutions, the university community, the nonprofit defense and environmental research community, and the profit-oriented industrial community are represented. It should be emphasized that Panel members participated as individuals and not as spokesmen for their fields or organizations.

3

The Panel's work was aided by the availability of numerous oceanographic reports and studies, some of which are cited herein. Sponsored primarily by the National Academy of Sciences and the Interagency Committee on Oceanography, these reports have greatly aided formulation of the Panel's recommendations. Considerations of marine biology appeared especially important in evaluating the national program. Because of this, a subpanel under the chairmanship of William D. McElroy was formed to examine problems and prospects in biological oceonography. This subpanel met as a group on 11 days (see app. I).

Meeting for formal sessions on 18 days, the PSAC Panel heard about 50 invited experts and agency representatives. Early meetings were devoted to gathering information about the scope, content, and nature of the wide range of activities being conducted in and on or associated with oceans. Opinions about future actions were sought, and consideration was given to limitations and constraints imposed by manpower, funds, prospects of economic returns, and laws or the lack thereof. In general, these meetings were held at places where oceanography or related scientific work was being conducted. Smaller groups under Panel members' leadership also worked in such areas as the law of the sea and technological possibilities for seagoing or underwater engineering.

In addition to formal Panel activities, individual members visited facilities, discussing oceanography with interested members of the scientific and industrial communities. Indeed, it is not an exaggeration to state that many Panel members have devoted a substantial part of the past year to these activities. A more complete listing of Panel activities is given in appendix I.

There are limitations on this report. It is not a blueprint with detailed projects or activities whch would constitute a national ocean program for the years to come. Rather, it is an attempt to identify the current problems of national interest and to present a framework within which program details can be most effectively planned by those responsible for carrying them out. We have identified important opportunities which such a program should recognize and attempt to exploit and have given an assessment of the priority which we feel should be attached to the national ocean program as a whole and to its expected major components.

4

2.0. Food From the Sea

2.1. INTRODUCTION

Adequate nutrition is prerequisite to all other human activities. For most of humanity, life is supported by a diet which is largely, if not exclusively, of vegetable origin. Only in the developed areas is a significant fraction of calories and of proteins and vitamins supplied by food stuffs of animal origin. Approximately 1.5 billion persons, largely in the tropical and subtropical zones, live on diets which are frequently dominated by one staple crop although occasionally mixtures of vegetables and cereals are available. But many vegetable diets fail to provide protein either of the quantity or the quality needed for adequate human nutrition. The quality of protein depends on its composition of amino acids. Vegetable proteins frequently are absolutely or relatively deficient in one or another of the ten amino acids essential for human nutrition. For example, corn is seriously deficient in tryptophan and is not adequate in lysine content.

Chronic protein deficiency, the consequence of inadequate amino acids in the diet, is a serious public health problem of man. Combined with infectious diseases whose effects it magnifies, this form of malnutrition is the leading cause of death in the period between weaning and 5 years of age in all countries in the equatorial zone. Protein deficiency accounts for as high as 50 percent of deaths at these ages. Protein deficiency also limits the lifespan and productive capacity of adults. If these peoples are to be assisted in their entry into the 20th century, if they are to be offered opportunity on the scale available to developed nations, it is imperative that their diets be improved, particularly with respect to protein.

Several techniques for nutritional improvement are apparent. One of these is to redistribute agricultural products to assure that, instead of a single staple, a mixture of vegetables and vegetable products with a balanced amino acid composition is consumed regularly. Experiments are in progress but to accomplish this redistribution on a large scale would be an enormous task.

The second technique is to provide a nutritional supplement of 10 to 20 grams of animal protein per day to a predominantly vegetable

5

diet. The specific animal protein is of little consequence. Beef, pork, chicken, rabbit, fish, mollusks, and crustaceans—any will serve. In fact, if man is to be adequately nourished, each source must be exploited to the fullest. The relative inefficiency, however, of converting agriculturally produced grains and grasses into animal protein, i.e., beef, pork, or chicken, makes it increasingly difficult to use these animal proteins to supply the needs of a hungry world with a rapidly increasing population.

The available projected growth of world population indicates that the nations of the world will be hard pressed to meet caloric needs from conventional agriculture, ignoring the problem of providing reasonable amounts of animal protein (table 2.1). For example, one estimate states that [1] "the new mouths in the underdeveloped world will need some 300 million tons of additional grain annually by 1980—an amount approaching the present total production of North America and Western Europe combined." Obviously neither our present surplus farm capacity nor a markedly increased effort here and in other developed countries can meet the growing nutritional needs of the world's population. Before long a major portion of the food supply must be produced in the very countries where it is needed. Unfortunately, experiences in underdeveloped nations indicate that it is difficult to upgrade local agriculture to levels of production achieved in the United States and in Western Europe. Improvement of living standards in developing nations which have gained political independence but have yet to achieve industrial development cannot be expected unless their people are adequately nourished.

TABLE 2.1.—*Projected World Population and Annual Protein Demands*

	1900	1920	1940	1950	1960	1980	2000
Population (billions)	1.55	1.81	2.21	2.51	2.91	4.22	6.27
Annual:							
Protein demand (billion pounds):							
Animal				20.0	23.6	33.9	50.3
Pulses				30.2	35.3	50.9	75.6
Cereal				90.3	105	153	227
Total				141	164	238	353

It is for these reasons that the Panel considers it imperative that a third technique, full exploitation of the opportunities for obtaining food from the sea, be attempted as rapidly as possible. These opportunities are commensurate with the magnitude of the nutritional prob-

---

[1] *International Science and Technology*, December 1965.

lem in the world. In 1964, the world fish catch contained 17.1 billion pounds of protein (based on wet weight of fish containing 15 percent protein), an amount which would have supplied slightly more than 10 grams of protein per day to 2 billion individuals, and would have been effective in eliminating or alleviating chronic protein deficiency for the people of the equatorial zones. That this opportunity for upgrading nutrition has not been adequately exploited, reflects cultural as well as economic barriers, failure of distribution, and inefficiencies of use.

2.2. PROTEIN PRODUCTION IN THE SEA

It is estimated that at least 400 billion tons of organic material, wet weight, are produced annually in the sea, only a tiny fraction of which is harvested by man. In the sea, as on land, food is produced by plants that utilize energy in sunlight to synthesize organic materials from inorganic substances. The "grass" of the sea, composed of microscopic plants (phytoplankton) is eaten by the grazers (zooplankton) which in turn are consumed by larger animals such as fish. This is the food chain of the sea (see sec. 6.4).

Agriculture to be highly productive requires continual replenishment of plant nutrients through artificial fertilization. In the ocean, nutrients are replenished by natural processes such as regeneration due to microbial activities and inflow of fresh waters which contain nutrients from the land including agricultural fertilizers and sewage. With the death of animal and plantlife in the sea, the organisms sink and are decomposed, releasing nutrients. These nutrients are concentrated in bottom waters where, due to the absence of light, they cannot be used for photosynthesis. In areas of upwelling, the nutrient-rich bottom waters are brought to the surface where they sustain large populations of phytoplankton. Wherever this occurs, such as in the Humboldt current off the coast of Peru, phytoplankton flourish and a vigorous food chain is sustained, leading to the production of large quantities of fish.

2.3. THE WORLD FISH CATCH

The present world fish catch is about 114 billion pounds (table 2.2). The magnitude of the catch is dependent upon many factors, among which are the rate of production of fish in a given area and intensity of harvest. These factors vary for different species and for different areas of the ocean. The catch increased from 60.5 billion to 114 billion pounds in the last 10 years. It is uncertain how large a crop can be harvested. The most dramatic instances of increased catches in recent years have resulted from finding new fishery stocks. Indeed, the most dramatic has been off the coast of Peru, where a catch of 20

TABLE 2.2.—*Annual Fish Catch* [1] (*in Billion Pounds*) *for Leading Countries and for the World From 1954 to 1964* [2]

	1954	1955	1956	1957	1958	1959	1960	1961	1962	1963	1964
Peru	0.43	0.52	0.71	1.12	2.15	4.83	7.87	11.7	15.3	15.2	20.2
Japan	10.0	10.8	10.5	11.9	12.1	13.0	13.7	14.8	15.1	14.8	14.0
China	5.06	5.55	5.83	6.87	8.93	11.0	12.8				
U.S.S.R.	4.98	5.50	5.78	5.58	5.78	6.08	6.72	7.17	7.97	8.33	9.87
United States	6.13	6.15	6.59	6.08	5.97	6.37	6.19	6.46	6.55	6.13	5.82
Norway	4.47	4.00	4.83	3.85	3.18	3.48	3.41	3.35	2.94	3.06	3.54
World	60.5	63.5	67.1	69.3	72.4	80.1	87.1	94.6	102	105	114

[1] Data are total commercial catches including invertebrates and fresh water fish.
[2] Data from *Yearbook of Fishery Statistics*, Food and Agriculture Organization of the United Nations, vol. 18.

8

billion pounds of anchovy was taken in 1964 whereas 10 years previously the catch had only been 2 percent of that amount. Even though relatively primitive techniques are used for harvesting anchovy, the resource may have been overfished and the Peruvian government has this year restricted the catch to 15 billion pounds as a step to assure a continuing and stable harvest.

The U.S. fish catch for the last 30 years has been about 6 billion pounds which does not include sport fishery catches. The sport fishery catch in coastal and marine waters was estimated at 590 million pounds in 1960.[1]

Additional resources are present in waters off the U.S. coasts. It is estimated that a standing crop of about 15 billion pounds of hake and anchovy is present in the California current off the coasts of California, Oregon, and Washington. Until recently, this resource has not been utilized because, for one reason, anchovy are food for sport fishes, and sportsmen are concerned that intensive fishing on anchovy might disrupt sport fishery populations. An agreement has now been worked out by the California Fish and Game Commission to allow some 150 million pounds to be harvested in 1966 for processing into fishmeal and oil. If properly managed, these hake and anchovy populations might yield an annual catch of 2 or 3 billion pounds.

Fishery resources in all parts of the world, especially in those areas near populations with protein deficiencies, have not been studied as thoroughly as those in the California Current. Therefore, it is difficult to predict the maximum harvest and the amount of food potential now present in the world's oceans. Some estimates indicate that the world's fish catch might be increased three or four times. More optimistic estimates predict a tenfold increase. One pertinent fact is that the fish catch in the last 20 years has increased at a faster rate than the world's population.

2.4. UTILIZATION OF FISH FOR HUMAN CONSUMPTION

Whereas certain fishes are brought to market directly for human consumption, a large fraction of the total fish catch is not utilized directly by man. This is particularly true of fishes of relatively moderate and small size—e.g., anchovy, menhaden, and hake—which are caught in great numbers by simple trawling and seining procedures. These "industrial fish" are processed for oil and fish meal. Fishmeal is used as a high protein source for poultry and livestock feeds. From the standpoint of human nutrition, this use is wasteful because some of the protein in fish is lost in its conversion to poultry and livestock protein.

---

[1] *Sport fishing—today and tomorrow.* Outdoor Recreation Resources Review Commission Report 7. 1962.

9

Nevertheless, the problems of storage and transportation, rapid spoilage, costs of processing small fish, and the cultural habits of many people, make it apparent that only a small fraction can be utilized directly as food by man. The major portion of the catch, such as the small sized fish which abound in the Humboldt Current or off the California coast, must be processed into a form which is readily stored and transported and acceptable as food by peoples of many cultures. The Bureau of Commercial Fisheries has developed a solvent extraction process for preparation of a marine protein concentrate from various species of hake. The resultant product, which is 85 percent protein, is highly nutritious and almost tasteless and odorless. It is estimated that this material can be produced commercially for about 25 cents per pound. A ton of hake when processed yields 320 pounds of concentrate containing about 250 pounds of protein—an animal protein supplement of 10 grams per day for 30 people at a cost of $2 per person annually.

It is unclear how many other species of animals in the oceans might be utilized similarly. Intensive exploration and research on artificial cultivation of marine organisms might well lead to new sources of such protein concentrates.

There remains, however, the very serious problem of getting the people in some underdeveloped nations to accept marine protein concentrates. The few attempts which are known to the Panel have not been successful. Since the problem of protein malnutrition is most acute in young children, it would appear that a great and important opportunity of using marine protein concentrate is being overlooked. Fortification of processed foods for children of the "breakfast cereal" type, with marine protein concentrate, should be acceptable to young children and also invaluable in protecting their health.

2.5. AQUICULTURE

Although the opportunities to enrich and amplify man's food supply by fishing in the open sea are highly significant, they are, nevertheless, limited. An entirely different set of opportunities is offered, however, by the potential crop that might be obtained by systematic and scientific farming of restricted areas of the sea—"aquiculture." As noted above, the yield of fish in some areas of the sea depends largely on the nutrients supplied by upwelling. Attempts can now be undertaken, at least on a pilot scale, to utilize natural hydrodynamic or atmospheric energy sources to bring to the surface nutrient-rich deep water to fertilize selected marine habitats such as bays or coral lagoons. The problems involved are technological as well as biological and their solution requires a marriage of engineering and marine biology on a scale not attempted previously. In a general way, two large problems must be solved: (a) means of using hydrodynamic or atmospheric energy to drive the artificial upwelling which is desired, and (*b*) control of the amount of nutrients delivered so desirable phytoplankton are produced, and so that excess production of organic matter does not exceed the carrying capacity of the environment, specifically for oxygen, causing mass mortality of marine life (see sec. 6.4).

Some of the most appealing opportunities for aquiculture exist in our estuaries and coastal waters, regions which are most accessible and amenable to control and management. Unfortunately, in places these waters are being overfertilized from nutrients in sewage discharge. Regulation and control of such nutrients, to the same extent as that required in any deliberate fertilization practice, could potentially transform what is now a public health hazard and a national disgrace into the opportunity for production of valuable marine products (see sec. 3.4).

In view of the obvious need for more protein to feed the world population, the Panel *recommends* that attempts be made to augment the food supply through marine aquiculture. This recommendation is made with the full realization that little of the necessary technological knowledge is currently available, but the dire need for increased protein production in the world, nevertheless, argues strongly that we should encourage the development of a strong research program that will be needed for effective aquiculture. At this time the U.S. effort in marine aquicultural research is essentially nonexistent except for limited studies on oysters, clams, and shrimp.

Current Attempts at Aquiculture. Japan is the current world leader in marine aquiculture. Its efforts have been directed to production of organisms with a high market value such as fish, shrimp, and shellfish, including oysters for pearl culture, and have not attempted to produce low-cost food. Japan's success is indicated by the data in table 2.3. Limited experiments on farming the sea in Scottish lochs have indicated that fish production can be increased by fertilization, in some cases as much as 16 to 18 times. However, the scale of these experiments was relatively small. The yields of fish grown in unfertilized ponds in different areas of the earth are similar to cattle and swine production. If the waters are fertilized, the yields of fish are much greater (table 2.4) and are comparable with yields obtained from converting agricultural crops into domestic livestock.

Oysters, Clams, and Other Phytoplankton Feeders. Because energy is lost at each step in the food chain (i.e., not all of the food eaten is transformed into new, living material), it is evident that animals which feed directly on phytoplankton are most promising as efficient protein producers. Oysters, clams, and other shellfish are such phytoplankton feeders.

Oyster culture was started in Japan and in France 300 and 100 years ago, respectively. It involves finding suitable spawning and

11

TABLE 2.3.—*Harvest and value of sea fisheries and aquiculture in Japan in 1963* [1]

	Sea fisheries		Aquiculture	
	Harvest	Value	Harvest	Value
	Billion pounds [2]	*Million dollars*	*Million pounds*	*Million dollars*
1951	8.3		193	
1952	10.2		225	
1953	9.7		317	
1954	9.5		320	
1955	10.3		340	
1956	9.8		397	
1957	11.2		529	
1958	11.5		472	
1959	12.3	739	497	64
1960	12.8	892	625	94
1961	13.9	1,000	687	126
1962	14.1	1,070	797	149
1963	13.6	1,190	857	180

[1] Data from "Fisheries Statistics of Japan 1963," Statistics and Survey Division, Ministry of Agriculture and Forestry. Government of Japan. 1965.
[2] Average for years 1945–50 was 5.5 billion pounds.   [3] Average for years 1945–50 was 90 million pounds.

seeding areas, collecting larvae on artificial surfaces and transplanting seed into bays, estuaries, and ponds that have rich algal growths which favor rapid growth to commercial size. Private concerns in many parts of the United States culture oysters, but to a great degree we still exploit and try to preserve the natural beds. The production of oysters on the U.S. west coast is based almost solely on seed imported from Japan.

Forty years ago the Japanese began growing oysters on long ropes hanging from floating rafts or on ropes sustained by buoys. The difference in production is astounding: the old method yielded annually no more than 600 pounds per acre, while the raft method yields as much as 16,000 to 32,000 pounds per acre. With the new method, oysters are grown throughout the water column, not only on the bottom; therefore, oysters free from bottom predators grow rapidly even when the bottom is unsuitable for their development.

In Japan oysters are bred and selected for flavor and maximum yield. Progress was rapid after suitable methods were discovered for feeding oyster larvae artificially on cultured algae. A similar research program for growing clams is in progress at the Bureau of Commercial Fisheries Laboratory, Milford, Conn.

In the United States, the Public Health Service has identified areas, totaling more than 10 million acres, that are suitable for shellfish production. Only about 7 million acres were in production in 1964— the unused acres were inactive due to pollution and other causes. It

TABLE 2.4.—*Annual production, live weight of animals in pounds per acre* [1]

	Animal	Yield (Average or range)
Sea water, unfertilized: [2]		
Fishponds, Philippines	Milkfish	400–980
Fishponds, France	Grey mullet	300
Fishponds, Java	Milkfish	
Poorest		40
Richest		300
Fishponds, Indonesia	Milkfish	140
	Prawns	46
	Wild fish	23
North Sea, 1922	Fish	21.3
World marine fishery [3]	do	0.45
Adriatic [4]	do	4.6
Middle Atlantic Continental Shelf [4]	do	61.9
Humboldt Current, Peru [6]	Anchovy	300
Chesapeake Bay [5] oyster bottom	Oyster	600
Sea water, fertilized: [2]		
Fishponds, Formosa	Milkfish	1,000
Brackish water, fertilized:		
Experimental fish farm, Palestine	Carp	755–7,970
Commercial ponds, Palestine	do	356–4,210
Land:		
Cultivated land	Swine	450
Grassland	Cattle	5–250

[1] Data unless otherwise indicated from C. H. Mortimer and C. F. Hickling, "Fertilizers in Fishponds." Fishery Pub. No. 5, 1957. London: Her Majesty's Stationery Office.

[2] Ponds constructed so that sea water can enter through gates. Gates can be closed to contain fish.

[3] C. L. Cutting. Economic aspects of utilization of fish. Biochemical Society Symposium No. 6. Biochemical Society. Cambridge, England.

[4] Range of values for selected ocean areas listed by H. W. Graham and R. L. Edwards. 1961. Fish in nutrition.

[5] J. L. McHugh. In press. In *Symposium on Estuaries*. American Association for Advancement of Science.

[6] M. B. Schaefer. 1965. Transactions American Fisheries Society. Vol. 94, pp. 123–128.

is informative to make some calculations concerning potential oyster production in these areas. If 600 pounds were produced per acre, the yield in Japan and in Chesapeake Bay under natural conditions, then the total U.S. production would be 6 billion pounds annually or about equal to the present U.S. fish catch (table 2.2). If the production rate in these areas were increased 15 times, the yield would be 90 billion pounds a year or nearly equal the present world fish catch. A 15-fold increase does not seem unrealistic since the Japanese have increased yields as much as 50-fold. The yield of oysters is apparently limited by their food supply. If production of suitable kinds of phytoplankton could be increased by artificial fertilization (see sec. 6.4), even greater yields might be realized or greater areas might become available for exploitation.

Shrimp and Crab. A successful method has been developed in Japan to culture large prawns. It requires indoor culturing of new-born larvae which are fed first on diatoms and then on tiny brine shrimp. In a month the larvae are almost an inch long and are ready to be cultivated in artificial ponds formerly used for salt production. Adults are produced in 1 year by being fed ground shellfish and scrap fish. The present complex technique is commercially profitable in Japan because the Japanes gourmet is willing to pay $2 to $4 per pound for live shrimp. For similar size shrimp, the U.S. fisherman receives from 50 to 80 cents per pound for the tails alone. This is the first commercial trial in Japan, and cheaper cultivation techniques will undoubtedly be found.

The complete life cycles of several species of crabs are known in the United States, opening the way for artificial cultivation. Attempts are now underway to rear spiny lobsters in Japan.

Squid. Squid are a delicacy for the Japanese and Mediterranean peoples. In Japan five species of squid are cultured in the laboratory. Growth in culture is faster than in nature; commercial squid weighing a pound or more are obtained in 3 to 5 months. Probably, more rapid growth can be obtained by further refinement of techniques and by continuous feeding. It is interesting that squid can be reared and maintained alive for months in captivity, whereas captured adults die in a few weeks.

Phytoplankton Production. Since organic productivity rests on the energy-trapping ability of the plants in the sea, basic and applied research on the ecology of ocean pastures should be fostered. This research is needed if selected areas of the sea are to be farmed.

Mass culturing of marine phytoplankton is feasible because the main nutritional requirements are known. It should be possible to produce large quantities of phytoplankton in lagoons and artificial coastal lakes. Algae could also be grown in floating plastic tanks or in gigantic submerged plastic sausages. Basic requirements for growing algae are ponds or large containers and relatively small amounts of nutrients to add to the water.

Phytoplankton production under controlled conditions is essential for development of marine aquiculture. Many economically important organisms feed on phytoplankton either throughout life (e.g., oysters and clams) or during early stages of development (newborn shrimp larvae eat phytoplankton and later become carnivorous). Algae are also needed for food for the shrimplike creatures which constitute the bulk of the zooplankton—the food of many economically important marine animals.

Research is needed to identify algal species having high food values and rapid growth rates. Preliminary research indicates that manipulation of growth conditions and nutrients can induce accumulation of particular components altering, for instance, the protein-fat ratio of algae. This metabolic flexibility, in addition to offering the possibility of tailoring composition to suit predators' nutrition, may provide new means of obtaining high yields of fats, sterols, antibiotics, and vitamins (see sec. 6.4).

2.6. SUMMARY

No one of the approaches outlined above will suffice. The total demand for animal protein by the world's population cannot be met adequately for many years, probably not until the turn of the century when, it would be hoped, the world's population will have been stabilized and agricultural and aquicultural technology will have had an opportunity to catch up. We cannot expect to close this gap unless we begin now.

Clearly, the United States lags behind other nations in the technology of fishing and aquiculture. Future food problems of the world require that we develop these technologies and assist other nations to develop them. The Panel assigns very high priority to this task and further notes that to foster the needed technology, at least in the early stages, will require support by the Federal Government, both in its own laboratories and in extramural institutions.

3.0. Modification of the Ocean Enviroment

3.1. INTRODUCTION

Man can and does interfere with the oceans and atmosphere in a number of different ways, thus, in a sense environmental modification is already a reality. In oceans, man's ability to produce deliberate, beneficial changes is still very limited. For example, he can attempt to alter the configuration of the coastline, although the results are not always predictable. Besides deliberate modification, there is the inadvertent modification in which we know man is participating to an increasing extent, but the consequences are too little known.

3.2. GENERAL CONSIDERATIONS

"The Nation behaves well if it treats the natural resources as assets which it must turn over to the next generation increased and not impaired in value."—*President Theodore Roosevelt.*

"Our conservation must not be just classic protection and development, but a creative conservation of restoration and innovation."—*President Lyndon B. Johnson, in his message on Natural Beauty.*

Today, as nearly a century ago, the Federal Government recognizes the need to treat our natural resources as assets. As the complexity of society increases, it becomes more difficult to protect, preserve, and conserve these resources. Programs are needed for marine as well as terrestrial, atmospheric, and fresh water environments.

Continuing population growth combined with increased dependence on the sea for food and recreation means that modification of marine environments will not only continue, but will drastically increase. New technological developments such as atomic power reactors, sea level canals, weather modification and desalinization plants lead to new forms of modification. We are far from understanding most short-range and all long-range biological consequences of environmental modification.

These considerations suggest that we now need to preserve the quality of as much of the unmodified or useful marine environment as we can and to restore the quality of as much of the damaged environment as possible. Delay will only increase the cost in money, time, manpower, resources, and missed opportunities.

3.3. SPECIFIC CONSIDERATIONS

Inadvertent modification occurs in many forms. The most widely spread and most pervasive ones are various kinds of pollution. Pollutants include garbage, sewage, agricultural and industrial wastes, pesticide and herbicide residues, and waste heat. Future pollutants may include radioactive waste from nuclear reactors and salt wastes from desalinization plants.

The marine environment is particularly susceptible to pollution because most avenues of disposal terminate in the oceans. In the past, pollution of the oceans has been of little concern because the oceans have always been considered so large. However, most pollution occurs at the margins where human activities are centered and the concentrated wastes remain for varying times in this region before dispersal into the vast open ocean. Moreover, the potential for pollution is increasing as more of man's activity is concerned with the oceans. It was once thought that rivers could not be polluted seriously, but the truth is now obvious. It is also becoming evident that large bodies of water such as the Great Lakes can be drastically altered and reduced in value as natural assets. We have paid a great price to learn these lessons and should not make similar mistakes as we inhabit and exploit the oceans.

Fishing and other means of harvesting plant and animal populations have produced dramatic changes in distribution and abundance of marine organisms. Classical cases in this category are found among the marine mammals: especially baleen whales in the Antarctic; blue California gray whales; sea otters; fur seals, and southern and northern elephant seals. Habitat destruction by improper fishing techniques have affected our biological resources. An example of the latter is oysterbed destruction.

Introduction of organisms into areas has sometimes been extremely successful and valuable. Atlantic oyster culture in Nantucket and Martha's Vinyard sounds off Cape Cod and importing Japanese seed oysters to the Pacific Northwest are examples. In other cases introductions have been disastrous. Predatory Japanese snails introduced into the Black Sea in 1949 virtually eliminated mussel populations and apparently caused a sharp decline in flounder fisheries. Introductions have been planned or inadvertent. A great number of inadvertent introductions into the Atlantic and Pacific Oceans may result from opening the proposed sea-level canal across Central America. Deliberate modification of the coastline, such as channel dredging for marinas, shoreline modification for beach stabilization and filling in marsh areas for developmental purposes, pose serious problems. These modifications are occurring in estuaries which are important natural resources for recreation and food production. These areas are the nursery gounds for many marine organisms. How severely these and other environmental alterations affect the biota is unknown.

Finally, if weather modification becomes a reality, we can anticipate large-scale alteration of the marine environment in ways never possible previously. Changes in rainfall patterns on the land, shifts in wind distribution and changes in air temperature may produce persistent changes in near-shore salinity distributions, in patterns of wind-driven currents and in water temperature distribution. Subtle changes as far as man is concerned in the physical environment may greatly affect biological populations. Invasion of west Greenland waters by Atlantic codfish and probably the recent disappearance for commercial purposes of California sardines are examples of what may result from natural environmental fluctuations or a combination of natural and manmade effects.

3.4. WHAT NEEDS TO BE DONE

Five courses of action should be undertaken by the Federal Government:

1. *Establish a system of marine wilderness preserves as an extension to marine environments of the basic principle established in the Wilderness Act of 1964* (Public Law 88-577) that "it is the policy of the Congress to secure for the American people of present and future generations the benefits of an enduring resource of wilderness." In the present context, specific reasons for such preserves include:

(*a*) Provision of ecological baselines against which to compare modified areas.

(*b*) Preservation of major types of unmodified habitats for research and education in marine sciences.

(*c*) Provision of continuing opportunities for marine wilderness recreation.

2. *Undertake large-scale efforts to maintain and restore the quality of marine environments.* Goals of these efforts should include increasing food production and recreational opportunities and furthering research and education in marine sciences. A multiple-use concept should be evolved for marine environments analogous to that used for many Federal land areas (see Public Law 88-607, sec. 5B). It should be emphasized that this concept includes the recognition that for some areas, such as wilderness, only one use is possible.

3. *Increase research on biological effects of present and anticipated marine-environment modifications.* This research should take into account local, reversible, small-scale effects and large-scale, essentially irreversible, regional effects. Efforts should be made to predict biological effects of proposed or planned modifications so the effects can be assessed and evaluated prior to modification.

18

4. *Increase research on application of biological knowledge to rectify and alleviate undesirable consequences of environmental alteration.* Solutions could lead to positive assets. For example, growing shellfish and other organisms in marine waters fertilized by effluents from sewage treatment plants would improve water quality, and the organisms could be used as animal-food supplements or as fertilizer for plant crops.

5. *Insure that possible biological consequences are considered in planning environmental modification affecting marine environments, especially but not only for weather modification.* Obviously, the long-term as well as the short-term effects of environmental alterations should be considered in this context.

3.5. SUMMARY

Man's ability to modify and alter the marine environment necessitates (1) establishment of a system of marine wilderness preserves, (2) large-scale efforts to restore and maintain the quality of already damaged environments, (3) increased research into possible biological effects of environmental modification, and (4) advance consideration of biological effects of proposed programs that might cause environmental modifications.

4.0. Undersea Technology

Developments in undersea technology traditionally have resulted from:

1. Navy operational requirements.
2. Industrial attempts to create new business opportunities in and under the ocean.
3. Government-supported developmental efforts aimed at providing a higher level of services to ocean-based users.[1]

This division reflects the apportioning of responsibilities into:

1. National security.
2. Commercial exploitation.
3. Government-provided service.

This division of responsibility has proven successful in the past, and it will be a good pattern for the future. Accordingly, our appraisal of technology assumes a continuing role of present participants (see sec. 10.2.)

The following survey and appraisal of future opportunities is limited to undersea operations in the nonmilitary sector. The Navy's problems and roles are discussed in section 5, while problems in food production from the sea are considered in section 2. For purposes of this discussion, we consider "technology" to be the proven, existing capability whether or not the hardware is commercially available.

Our review of the status of undersea technology, as well as this Panel's overall recommendations, was greatly aided by results of a conference held September 20–23, 1965, involving Government and industry under the auspices of the Ocean Science and Technology Advisory Committee of the National Security Industrial Association. The conference was held at the request of the PSAC Panel on Oceanography and the Chairman of ICO. The conference report, together with a list of attendees, is given in appendix III.

---

[1] The intense and continuing government-industry interest in undersea technology is indicated by a few representative references: "Proceedings, Government-Industry Oceanographic Instrumentation Symposium," ICO, 1961; "Ocean Engineering," 6 vols. R. D. Terry, editor, published by North American Aviation in response to request from Chairman of ICO, 1964; "Buoy Technology," transcript of Marine Technology Society Symposium, 1964.

4.1. MATERIALS

A continuing need exists to provide vehicles with large working volumes at atmospheric pressures to protect instruments, equipment and personnel deep below the ocean.

In 1966 we are limited to using HY80 and maraging steels for the pressure containers. By 1970 high-strength titanium alloys will be commercially available, and in the 1975–80 period high-strength glass and cast ceramics will come into general use. Rapid progress is also being made in composite and fiber-reinforced materials.

The materials problem is difficult, and progress will be slow because of testing requirements; but solutions required for ocean applications are definitely on the way and should be available in time to accomplish missions which the Panel foresees.

4.2. INSTRUMENTS AND TOOLS

Navigational Problems. A need exists in the mineral industry to locate a point on the surface with an accuracy of:

1. 30 feet from a stationary ship within sight of land in order to exploit an entire lease or other mining claim without leaving a 150-foot (or more) border around the claim.

2. 150 feet from a stationary ship on the high seas in order to locate and return to a point accurately.

3. Ultimately 30 feet when underway for survey and research applications.

The best available commercial navigational equipment when utilized within sight of shore gives an accuracy of about 150 feet. It is possible today, by using extreme care from a stationary ship, to better this, but it is expensive because it requires precision geodesy to locate reference points and perfectly tuned beacons coupled with good conditions. Several systems including optical radar are under development which have not had sufficient testing to be operational and for which commercial equipment will not be available in less than 3 to 5 years. Within 10 years surface navigational accuracy of better than 100 feet underway will be available.

4.3. POSITIONING PROBLEMS

Drilling and construction activities require the ability to locate a bottom point to a position of better than 10 feet when referred to a point on the surface in the same vicinity.

Depending upon the depth of water and currents beneath the ship, conventional plumb-bob techniques provide adequate accuracy for determining bottom positions on a relative basis. On occasion, however, it is desirable, having located the specific spot on the bottom, to return precisely to it. In the case of deep drilling, MOHOLE research and development indicate that we can reenter deep-line drill holes if we plan in advance to do so. The MOHOLE techniques are good for this purpose, but are too expensive for conventional needs such as oil wells.

Humble Oil Co., in the Gulf of Mexico, has demonstrated an accuracy of precision in location by drilling to within a few feet of a 10-inch diameter pipe from a horizontal distance of 1 mile. This was necessary to cap a ruptured well by slant drilling and plugging with concrete. Although cost of surveying and guiding the drill was high, it was a remarkable feat of technology to do the job at all, even in shallow water.

4.4. IDENTIFICATION OF OBJECTS

In clear water under ideal conditions presently available optical image systems can give resolutions on the order of 1 inch at a range of 150 to 3,000 feet.

An important technological need is high-resolution imagemaking in turbid water. Some acoustical image systems in research today will not be available even as initial models for 2 or 3 years. The Panel estimates that within 10 years it will be possible to achieve resolution in turbid water using acoustical systems on the order of 10 feet in the range of 3,000 feet. While this is adequate to conduct surveillance under many conditions, it requires too close an approach for reconnaissance and adequate identification of many important objects. Presently there does not seem to be any good solution to the underwater visibility problem. What is needed is acquisition of 10-foot objects at 1 to 5 miles with a resolution of roughly 1 foot at a mile in muddy water. The development of adequate acoustical imaging systems will require the application of the most advanced optical imaging techniques.

4.5. TOOLS PROBLEM

As yet little has been done to make available the kinds of instruments and tools which would change the scope and nature of work performed by divers on the ocean floor. Examples of such devices are:

1. Nondestructive testing equipment to determine diagnostically the acceptability of components of bottom-mounted structures. A simple problem is reliability of a weld or porosity of a tube.

2. Tactile manipulators which give the diver (or ultimately the instrument-working platform) added strength and sensing abilities.

3. Semi-remote-control powered tools and support structures.

4.6. SERVICES

On land, Government traditionally provides many highly technical services for a wide variety of uses. We believe that these same services should be supplied to support ocean-going operations. The Panel has attempted to identify a most pressing technical need as seen by the users of these services.

Surveys. Good topographic and geologic surveys are needed. These surveys should first extend to the Continental Shelf of the United States. Second priority is given to other continental shelves, third priority to the deep ocean off the United States, and fourth rank to other deep-ocean areas. A major problem is to reduce the time and cost of surveying without reducing precision of the final result.

Using the best systems available today, it takes a single mothership plus small boats and a full crew an entire summer to chart the Martha's Vineyard-Nantucket Sound. It is uneconomical to consider doing the continental shelf of the world in this way. There are conceivably three ways of improving the technology of these surveys:

1. Development of a surface ship with much improved sensory equipment. This ship should be capable of taking differential data rapidly so that changes would be measured carefully, while data which vary slowly will be taken at a much slower rate. Both data taken and reduction should be automated so that final charts are produced in the original surveys. Present methods involving hand recording of many results indicate that this field is hampered by tradition.

2. Development of a submersible to carry out surveys. The submersible would do the entire job of maneuvering, sensing, data-taking, and reduction, thereby improving the accuracy of bottom topography and bypassing the surface-speed limitation which results from noise-suppression requirements. A major difficulty in such a scheme is accurate positioning of the submersible.

3. Development of towed or surface-commanded, free submerged platform to travel within perhaps 50 feet of the ocean surface. The towed body could be manned. Today's technology is adequate to build some sort of towed-body system, and the general opinion of industry is that by 1975 we can do bathymetry better, quicker, and more economically with submersibles than by following the present route.

In addition to the technological problems, topographic surveying is hampered by strict adherence to international conventions developed at a time when the technology was more primitive than it is today. Adequate surveying for the future will require a more realistic coupling of international convention with technolgy.

Forecasting. Ocean users inform us that we are not obtaining necessary weather data. The Michaelangelo incident provides one dramatic example of the need for short-term forecasts in the open oceans. The recent destruction of the British petroleum platform, with the resulting loss of 11 lives, has created new concern among undersea oil exploration companies. The basic problem in such sea operations is getting people off the rig when storms come. Large storms such as hurricanes take a long time to develop and are not as dangerous as more local storms having a shorter time scale. Present technology requires surface-mounted platforms, and users badly need data regarding predictions of wave height and local storms. Lacking these data, oil companies are presently designing platforms to operate from 50 to 150 feet below the surface of the sea, away from the weather.

The consensus of oil companies is that by 1975, if technology is available, most stationary installations will be on the bottom of the sea, not on the surface. Most drilling will probably be conducted from the surface, but oil well operations and some temporary storage facilities will be on the bottom. Presently, we do not have the technology needed for building installations on the ocean floor, but oil companies are determined to obtain it. They have estimated that about 10 years will be required to develop the technology and operating experience.

4.7. STANDARDS

Very few data and still fewer primitive, engineering standards now exist for underwater operations. If there is to be any substantial construction activity on the ocean floor as has been suggested, the following types of data and information must be provided:

1. An engineering characteristic for a variety of important bottom conditions to include standardized tests and their interpretation.

2. Environmental data on the water column (this is essentially the "weather in the sea" problem) and the relationship of water-column dynamics to bottom conditions.

3. Engineering standards for designing bottom-mounted structures in light of "sea-weather" data.

The Panel believes that in developing engineering standards for design and use in undersea installations, it is desirable to utilize competent, existing standard-making organizations. The Navy, the American Bureau of Shipping, and the American Standards Association Center should be the core of undersea standard-making activities. Specifically, the Panel does *not recommend* forming a new organization for the promulgation of engineering standards in the ocean environment.

One particular standard problem deserves mention. The Navy is presently the only organization equipped to certify submersibles. To date the Navy has certified only one such vehicle. Since the national requirement for developing deep-submergence capability in the next decade is clearly a Navy role, the Panel *recommends* that the Navy be the *only* agent to certify submersibles until undersea standardmaking organizations can develop the required competence and willingness to assume this responsibility.

The needs of industry for understanding bottom conditions and for describing weather within the sea in large measure parallel opportunities for scientific research discussed in sections 6.2 and 6.3.

4.8. SURF ZONE AND BEACH ENGINEERING PROBLEMS

The Nation needs to improve the technology for constructing coastal zone structures, which will make the national expenditure on breakwaters, harbors, beach erosion, docks, etc., more effective. The Panel was distressed to find a high failure rate of construction projects in the surf zone and on beaches, the destruction of beaches by breakwaters designed to extend the beaches, the silting of harbors and marinas as a result of construction designed to provide shelter, and the enhancement of wave action by the building of jetties supposed to lessen wave erosion are but a few examples of the inadequacy of our knowledge and practice in coastal construction. The Panel did not have sufficient time to draw major conclusions about these efforts but does offer the following observations:

1. The small budget of CERC (Coastal Engineering Research Center) cannot possibly underwrite the research and development program which is required to devise engineering techniques necessary for solving the difficult construction problems presented by the surf zone and beaches.

2. Engineering schools have been remiss in not participating in this problem through research projects proposed for governmental support.

3. The opportunity exists in many fine graduate departments in civil engineering and mechanical engineering to develop courses or specialty options which would lead to significantly higher levels of understanding and performance in near-shore construction projects, most of which are performed using public funds.

The university community should undertake responsibility for seeing that the best modern, engineering practice is being applied to publicly funded and executed surf zones and beach-construction projects.

4.9. BUOYS

Several scientific problems discussed in section 6.3 require deep-ocean buoys. In addition enhancement of weather-prediction capability will be in part based on observations from buoys. Thus, it is fortunate that buoy technology is developing rapidly. Buoys have been tethered and maintained in the deep sea for as long as 18 months. Buoy data can be tape recorded and telemetered on command from buoys to ship, to shore, and to satellite installations. The Panel believes it should be technically possible by 1975 to mount a World Weather Watch using buoys as sensing stations. This will not be possible, however, unless we soon begin to gather statistical experience with buoys. Too much effort has been expended, in the Panel's opinion, on obtaining an advanced buoy technology in a single step rather than in a broader program. There are also too many proposals for federally sponsored, buoy-experimental programs. What is required is a well-planned, evolutionary buoy-development program aimed at an operational World Weather Watch beginning in the 1975–80 time period.[2]

4.10. NEW LIGHTWEIGHT, COMPACT POWERPLANT

At present American undersea vehicles possess only an "elevator" capability. Purists may object to this statement, but the recent Spanish coast search operations force this conclusion. A small system of limited mobility would require a powerplant producing 10–100 kw. It seems reasonable that such a power system based on a fuel cell could be developed and be operational by 1975 if it were given sufficient priority by the Navy. For larger vehicles cruising at modest speeds (greater than 10 knots) for long times (weeks), however, it will be necessary to have reactor power sources in the 1–10 mw range. It is generally agreed that the present water reactor cannot be reduced in weight below 85 pounds per kilowatt where less than 50 pounds per kilowatt is required for the mission. No reactor technology which can meet this need is currently available, and in the Panel's view no private group is likely to undertake such a development during the 1965–80 time period.

The Panel does not believe that serious consideration should be given to concepts such as deep-ocean airplanes in the next decade. It will stretch our technology to the limit to build a versatile mobile platform from which two or three men can perform useful work in deep oceans.

---

[2] See app. II for a developmental program designed to use increasing buoy-system capacity to solve several scientific problems.

4.11. MAN IN THE SEA

Marine construction and maintenance operations in 1966 require free divers. The opinion of oil company staffs is that free divers will continue to be used where they can be put down and provided with tools to do useful work. Since oil and mining companies expect by 1975 that some operations will be conducted at depths byeond 1,500 feet, there will be a transition from divers to unmanned vehicles or manned instrumental platforms.

Oil industry needs clearly show many potential uses for man in the sea. Other users have requirements that demand a capability for men to live and work beneath the surface for extended periods. This capability may lead to new opportunities in the production of food either by fishing or aquiculture. Further, the interest of national security may make it necessary or strategically desirable to occupy areas of the oceans for extended periods.

Major groups of problems are associated with man living and working beneath the surface of the sea:

1. Problems directly related to survival, including biomedical problems and hazards from marine organisms.

2. Problems associated with design and operation of facilities for working while underwater. Certain of these problems have been considered earlier in this report.

Biomedical problems of survival are divisible into several categories. Most immediate are those produced directly by the wet, cold, dark, high-pressure climate. These include but are not restricted to an increased resistance to breathing during exertion and at rest; central nervous system narcosis by nitrogen and probably any other inert gas; long, slow decompression necessary for safe elimination of excessive inert gas from the tissues; toxicity of oxygen at high pressure; loss of body heat during prolonged submergence; and complex interactions of these factors. As the duration of man's underwater stay increases, additional problems appear. These include man's nutritional requirements under these rigorous conditions, composition and palatability of foods, psychological behavior of isolation and crowding in small spaces, and impairment of speech by unusual atmospheres. Medical procedures, including action of drugs on man in the sea, also require study. The similarity of certain of these problems to manned spaceflight is obvious, and advantage should be taken of this fact.

The presence of other sea organisms constitutes yet another group of complications. In many marine environments a variety of organisms are toxic if touched or eaten. Also, predatory forms such as sharks consider divers fair game.

Human survival underwater thus requires solution of a multiplicity of problems. Current knowledge in most of these areas is at best fragmentary; in some—especially long-term habitation problems—it is essentially nonexistent. Current research activity, directly applicable to oceangoing operations, is minimal in most of these areas.

Men working underwater require a wide range of support facilities. These include various underwater vehicles, underwater chambers in which to live and shore facilities for studying the effects of high pressure. Shore facilities should perhaps include high-pressure chambers for studies on man and animals, with capabilities to simulate depths of at least 1,000 feet.

Facilities are needed to meet the problem outlined above. In no university or private institution in the United States is there an extensive investigative program on the effects of very high pressures on man. The Navy is carrying out studies of man's long-term exposure to depths, but investigations are not primarily concerned with basic physiological effects at high pressure. Research of this type requires teams of trained specialists in medicine and biology and might best be conducted by a university medical center (see sec. 10.7).

The Panel does not foresee the need for a diver-operating capability in depths beyond 1,000 feet before 1975. At greater depths the diver will be replaced with highly instrumented platforms capable of maneuvering sensing devices, communicating with the surface and performing useful work. The technology being developed for space application may contribute substantially to unmanned operations at depth. Very likely these platforms will be manned and will require containers at atmospheric pressure.

4.12. MARINE MINING

The possibility of mining the sea floor has caught the popular imagination because of numerous articles and speeches about the potential riches of the sea. Mineral resources certainly exist under the oceans, but their economic potential varies enormously, depending on depth, location, and geological setting. Accordingly, we distinguish three general classes of minerals: Surface deposits on the shallow continental shelves; bulk deposits within the rocks under the shelves; and deposits on and in thin sediment layers of the deep sea floor (see also app. III.4).

The surface ore deposits of the Continental Shelf are mainly of two types, placer ores concentrated in submerged river channels and beaches and blanketing layers of nodules such as phosphorite, precipitated from sea water. These types of ores have been mined in various places around the world. Examples are: diamonds off Africa; tin off southeastern Asia; iron ores off Japan; and gold in many places. An attempt to mine phosphorite off California was apparently frustrated by a concentration of unexploded naval shells. Various countries have encouraged development of these ores by surveying their continental shelves. The Union of South Africa, New Zealand, and Australia, among others, have conducted or supported mineral surveys of the shelf. The United States is in the initial stages of such surveying, and we *recommend* that this program be accelerated. This is in line with our general recommendation that the Federal Government provide the same service in support of industry on the continental shelves as it does on land (see sec. 10.2). Development of new capabilities in undersea technology recommended in this report should greatly enhance the economic potential of mineral deposits discovered by Government surveys.

Geologically, rocks under the Continental Shelf differ in no significant manner from those of the adjacent continent. Hence, they probably contain the same mineral deposits. This has been confirmed by widespread exploitation of oil and gas. In a few places, moreover, mines have been extended from land under the sea. However, the economic potential of solid-mineral deposits within the submerged rock of the shelf appears minimal. The Geological Survey is determining the general structure of this submerged continental margin, and we *recommend* that this work be accelerated in order to bring it to the same level as geological mapping on land.

The deep-sea floor (under 2 or 3 miles of water) is paved in many places with nodules containing manganese, iron, cobalt, copper, and nickel in concentrations which approach the mineable levels on land. The potential resource is enormous, but the economic or mineable potential is certainly much less. The distribution, nature, and origin of the nodules are the subject of research presently supported by the Federal Government. In addition several mining companies have conducted special surveys of apparently promising deposits of nodules discovered in the course of oceanographic research. We consider this to be an appropriate division of Government and private effort and see no requirement for accelerated research on potential mineral resources of the deep-sea floor.

5.0. Ocean Science and Technology and National Security

5.1. INTRODUCTION

The most urgent aspect of Federal involvement in ocean science and technology for the next 5 to 10 years relates to national security in the narrow, strictly military sense. The U.S. Navy, which has responsibility for essentially all our defense efforts involving the ocean environment, will have increasing need for specialized oceanographic data for specific devices being developed or improved and will continue to require better understanding of characteristics of the ocean environment in which it operates.

In particular the Navy will need to improve the capabilities of its undersea strategic forces and ASW forces, as well as to increase its ability to perform undersea search and recovery. Improvement of the Navy's capabilities in these areas depends heavily on our national ability to discover and exploit new knowledge in ocean science and on our success in developing new and relevant ocean technology. Although everyone is aware in a general sense that ocean knowledge has military implications, the underlying reasons may not be widely understood. The military importance of oceanography entails an understanding of the nature of our national security programs, which themselves are not always completely comprehended.

Whereas the Navy's involvement in oceanography because of security and its often specialized interest will of necessity be distinct from that of other Government and private programs, the Navy must maintain working relations with all elements of the scientific and technological communities concerned. This relationship has been excellent in the past, correctly reflecting the Navy's deep interest in oceanographic research, and it should be strengthened in the future.

5.2. VITAL NAVY MISSIONS HEAVILY DEPENDENT ON OCEAN SCIENCE AND TECHNOLOGY

Antisubmarine Warfare. The submarine threat to the United States has been and is expected to remain a very serious consideration in defense planning. The Soviet Union now has a massive submarine force consisting both of nuclear and nonnuclear vessels. This force is being modernized and increased in size on an intense scale. Likewise, mainland China has already built several submarines, and even small powers such as North Korea and Egypt have conventionally powered submarine forces.

The massive Soviet submarine force threatens our naval forces and merchant shipping and its nuclear tipped missiles are capable of striking the continental United States. A more modest Chinese submarine force may develop in the next few years. To counter the threat from the U.S.S.R. the U.S. Navy is now spending and will undoubtedly continue to spend several billion dollars annually in operating and developing its antisubmarine forces. The effectiveness of these forces is limited in part by the incomplete understanding we have of environmental conditions in which antisubmarine sensors and weapon systems are employed. Considering the cost of operating our antisubmarine forces, an increase of a few percent in the effectiveness of these forces is worth several tens of millions of dollars a year.

Sensors used for detection, classification, localization, and tracking of submarines include active and passive sonar, Magnetic Anomaly Detection (MAD) and radar working in a very complex ocean environment. Their effectiveness depends heavily on environmental conditions in which they operate. We hardly have sufficient information on these conditions to do estimations and predictions sufficient for Navy needs.

Sonar provides a good example of the problems the environment imposes on our ASW forces. Sonar, both active and passive, is now and will probably remain the most important sensor for antisubmarine warfare. It can be designed to utilize several modes of underwater sound propagation. The effectiveness of these modes for any given piece of equipment and in any given situation depends *critically* on such detailed characteristics of the immediate ocean environment as the speed of sound (index of refraction), variation with depth, and absorption and characteristics of the ocean bottom and surface. These characteristics vary with locations and with time at any given position. Therefore, detection and classification ranges of a particular sonar system may vary tremendously from one time to another and from one location to another. These peculiarities must be understood and exploited to a great degree if we are to make our ASW forces as effective as possible.

The importance to ASW of a continuing, effective program to study and characterize the ocean environment in which its equipment is designed to operate cannot be overstated.

Strategic Forces. Development of long-range ballistic missiles in the last decade caused a revolution in the method of waging strategic warfare. Starting in late 1953 the United States engaged in an urgent program to build up its ballistic-missile forces. The U.S.S.R. embarked on the same kind of program even earlier. Missiles were originally contemplated as fixed devices on land.

At roughly the same time, however, the Navy undertook a program to develop a nuclear submarine and mounted a highly concerted and highly inventive weapon systems' development program to adapt ballistic missiles to it. The system, named Polaris, consists in essence of a small, solid rocket-ballistic missile launchable from a submerged nuclear submarine. Polaris, with a high degree of invulnerability, has become a fundamental building block for strategic forces. Indeed, a thought often expressed at the time was that ultimate nuclear stability would have both the U.S.S.R. and the United States equipped only with invulnerable Polaris forces and that neither side would have a ballistic-missile defense for population centers. In that way the outcome of a nuclear exchange would be clear and unmistakeable, and the possibility of a first nuclear strike even in critical times would be minimized.

The effectiveness of the submarine-based missile force is highly contingent on concealment, dispersion, high mobility, and very long patrol time. It is precisely for this reason that key interests of oceanography and the Navy, reflected in the development of the submarine-based strategic-missile force, have so much in common. With this relationship in mind the Navy instituted a special program of long-range research support for academic oceanography and intensified field studies by its own laboratories and ships. Even so, oceanographic research needs continuous and vigorous support from the Navy.

This research must cover on a massive scale the entire technological spectrum from basic and applied research to marine engineering. For example we must be able to verify that no presently unknown (to us) physical effects in the ocean environment make nuclear submarines susceptible to continuous tracking and location. Because of the possible increased emphasis in our strategic-defense capabilities in terms of the Navy's submarine-based missiles, and because this emphasis would only be well placed in the absence of any degradation of the submarines or of the enhancement of detection capability, the Navy must support a program which continuously explores all aspects of the ocean environment which conceivably could be exploited or utilized to allow continuous targeting of such submarines. If Polaris submarines could be continuously targeted, they would be open to premptive attack by ballistic missiles with relatively large warheads.

As enemy missile accuracy improves and as enemy missile payloads become more sophisticated, concealment and mobility become relatively more important. As we become increasingly concerned with penetrating enemy ballistic-missile defense, larger and more sophisticated payloads for our own strategic forces become increasingly important.

Development of the Poseidon Undersea Launching System will provide a significant improvement in our strategic capability in this regard. However, we can look forward to the need for even greater strategic capabilities in the future. Moreover, a submarine-based missile force has some less-than-ideal characteristics. It is relatively expensive to operate compared to land-missile forces; and it is presently limited in warhead size. Consequently, the ocean-based missile force could conceivably take some totally new direction of development in the future which would hopefully combine many of the better characteristics of the land-based force: Less expensive, larger payloads; better command and control, with some of the characteristics of the submarine force; i.e, invulnerability. This does not imply that we will not also have an interest in developing missile-carrying submarines capable of operating at much greater depths than currently. Perhaps the ocean bottom would help conceal their presence and thereby make them even less susceptible to enemy counteraction.

Such developments may, for example, take the form of missiles of Polaris' size or even considerably larger placed on relatively shallow underwater barge systems on the Continental Shelf in a way which conceals their location and requires the system to move infrequently so that the potential of its being tracked by motion-generated noise is minimized. In addition one might consider a slightly mobile ocean-bottom system which creeps along. Systems of this kind, if they are ever to be realized, will require different kinds of marine engineering research from that which produced the current submarine-based force. Such systems can involve much larger missiles, might require underwater maintenance by personnel also located underwater, might entail development of new kinds of implacement gear for positioning missiles, might necessitate new kinds of detection and survival equipment to prevent attacks on the implacements, and so on.

In summary it is very possible that the kind of strategic offensive force we may wish to develop for the future will rely even more heavily on ocean-based systems than that which we now have. Such systems may very well require operations at a much wider range of ocean environment and for much longer times than at present. Thus, the need for oceanographic research and support of these weapon systems becomes even greater and will certainly have to encompass a wider problem area in development and maintenance of present submarine forces. These problems will range from ascertaining that the ocean-based systems cannot easily be compromised by an enemy's exploitation of some hiterto hidden effects of the ocean's environment to development of massive ocean engineering capabilities. It is likely that the Navy's involvement in oceanographic research to develop, support, and maintain our weapon systems will increase rather than decrease in the future and will include a more widespread range of problems than it currently does.

Search and Recovery Exploration. Loss of the Thresher in 1963 and the recent search for the lost nuclear weapon in the Mediterranean off the Spanish coast cannot be regarded as insignificant, isolated incidents in long-term plans for national security. A continuing requirement will be seeking, identifying, and retrieving objects related to national defense from the ocean floor. These objects can be grouped roughly as follows:

1. Disabled submersibles with survivors.
2. Weapon system components, instruments, or data packages.
3. Hardware, recovery of which is based on economic considerations or diagnostic needs.
4. Debris, recovery of which is required for diagnostic purposes.

When life is at stake, it is essential to move quickly and to mobilize men and equipment at the site of the incident. In view of the sensitive nature of many of these tasks, the military research-recovery mission must be assigned to the Navy.

In order to carry out these missions the Navy should create a specially trained task force to cope with deep sea recovery. It must be continually on call and highly mobile so that the requisite force to initiate search operations can be assembled almost anywhere in the world within 24 hours. Technology required by this task force exists only in part and will have to be developed by the Navy in the next several years. In time the civilian sector will need some of this technology and eventually perhaps will conduct search and retrieval activities. Notwithstanding, the Panel *recommends* that all ocean search-and-recovery missions related in any way to national security be the responsibility of the Navy.

5.3. THE NAVY'S OCEANOGRAPHIC PROGRAM

The Navy's oceanographic program excluding the one-time ship-construction appropriation of a nuclear-powered deep-ocean engineering vehicle has expanded from $120 million in fiscal year 1965 to $141 million in fiscal year 1966 and to $205 million for fiscal year 1967. Although the program has been subdivided in many different ways, it can for the purposes of this report be divided into:

(*a*) Basic research and education;
(*b*) Research and development for undersea weapons and sensors;
(*c*) Mapping and charting;
(*d*) Undersea technology;

(e) Rescue, search, and recovery of undersea objects;

(f) Test and evaluation facilities;

(g) Oceanographic data and information services.

Basic research and education are so vital to both the Navy and the national interest in the marine environment that they will be discussed singly in the next subsection. Research and development for undersea weapons and sensors are the Navy's purview, and any discussion must take into consideration the Navy's requirements, which is beyond the scope of this Panel's assignment. The Panel does *recommend:*

1. Unclassified R & D information be made available in timely fashion.

2. Classified R & D information in the area of sensor development be made more available to Federal and industrial communities having application for the data than has been the case.

The judgment of the Panel is that current Navy classification policies often weigh short range and narrow security considerations too heavily as compared to the longer range security which must be gained by more rapid and effective development of the scientific and technological base from which its systems are derived. Our recommendation therefore is that the Navy review its classification policies with a view to furthering more rapid progress by increasing the diffusion of deep sea technology. While information that will compromise military systems must be classified, advantages of wide diffusion and input diversity from scientific and industrial communities generally outweigh any risk involved.

Mapping and charting, sometimes referred to as hydrographic surveys, are responsibilities of the Defense Intelligence Agency. Ocean mapping and charting by the Navy are executed as part of the total national oceanographic program. Military requirements dictate a greater degree of accuracy in charting the ocean bottom than is required by other Federal agencies. Therefore, no quantitative recommendations can be made with respect to the Navy's survey program requirements. However, criticism applicable to the survey program of ESSA is equally valid with respect to the Navy's Hydrographic Survey Program (see sec. 4–6). The Panel concurs on the recent action to establish an R & D program in Navy mapping and charting and *recommends:*

1. A minimum expenditure of $2 million per year in light of significant Navy expenditures in mapping and charting.

2. Continuation of commercial ship leasing for added survey requirements.

Undersea technology is that general area of ocean engineering not associated directly with specific defense systems. The ability to construct towers on the ocean floor, general undersea navigational concepts, and deep undersea materials technology form part of the Navy's undesea technology program. The Sea Bed (vol. 4) report recommended a substantial Navy program of several hundred million dollars' expenditure over the next several years in this area. The Panel *recommends* a significant increase over the present $2 million a year in Navy expenditures.

Shortly after the loss of the Thresher the Navy convened a board to evaluate and ascertain the Navy's ocean capabilities specifically with regard to submarine rescue. After a year-long study this group (Deep Submergence Systems Review Group) recommended establishment of a 5-year program having four basic areas, costing about $332 million. These four categories were specified for the Navy's concentrated effort:

1. Submarine location, escape and rescue;
2. Deep-ocean, small-object location and recovery;
3. Increased salvage capability;
4. Extended capabilities of man as a free swimmer to perform useful work in the ocean environment to his physiological limits.

As a result of these recommendations the Navy formed a special group called the Deep Submergence Systems Project which was to implement these capabilities and enable the Navy to have worldwide operational capabilities by 1969. This group, initially placed within the Navy's special project office, was recently made a separate CNM-designated project in order to focus the Navy's effort on exploration of oceanic depth. An additional task for this new group was management of the nuclear powered oceanographic vehicle (NR-1). The accomplishment of the four specific tasks initially given this group has been delayed in part because of funding problems. This year's budgeting for the prototype rescue vessel is approximately $3½ million short of the amount required; this difference is attributable to the low estimated cost at the onset of the program. This vehicle, now stripped of all significant search-and-recovery capability, will give us limited capability by the end of 1968 to rescue men from disabled submarines at their collapse depth. A full complement of six vehicles in 1970 will provide worldwide rescue capability. There exists today no demonstrated, operational capability to rescue personnel from submarines beyond a depth of 600 feet; this leaves a depth gap with no capability to rescue and no capability to rescue from under ice.

Search-and-recovery capability regarding small objects has suffered the most severe cutback. Initial recommendations to the Navy provided a capability to locate and recover small objects over 98 percent of the ocean floor (20,000 feet) by 1970. A worldwide operational capability in this field will require highly sophisticated, deep-diving search-and-recovery vehicles, supporting research and development and instrumentation. The experience off Spain in the recovery of the nuclear weapon illustrate the problems in the fields of acoustic detection and imaging, underwater navigation and marking devices and endurance and maneuvering capabilities in the vehicles (see secs. 4.1, 4.2, 4.3, 4.4). It was fully 3 weeks after the loss of the nuclear weapon before any deep-ocean equipment was on the scene and an adequate surface-navigation network established. This portion of the Navy's program is now limited to one R & D prototype search-test vehicle with limited depth capability. In the area of large-object salvage the initial goal, salvaging an attacked submarine from its collapse depth, has been restricted by lack of funds to a 1970 operational capability of 600 feet, the depth of the continental shelves. Backup studies will enable implementation of desired capabilities, should adequate funding be made available.

In the area of extending man's capabilities as a free swimmer at desired depths, the Navy is performing only the minimum necessary, specific physiological research and development through controlled experiments in shore-based pressure facilities (see sec. 4.11). This work is supported by a series of experiments (Sea Lab 1 and 2 being completed and Sea Lab 3 scheduled for February 1967). These experiments are expected to continue until there is a demonstrated capability as deep as 1,000 feet.

In summary the four specific areas of effort recommended by the Deep Submergence Systems Review Group to the Secretary of the Navy regarding implementation and operational capabilities continue to be hampered by funding limitations. A worldwide rescue capability will be available in 1970. There is no planned capability for locating and recovering small objects from ocean depths beyond 6,000 feet (the mean depth of the ocean is 12,000 feet). The effort to extend free-swimmer capability into depths is proceeding on schedule but lacks adequate physiological and biomedical research (see sec. 4.11). The Navy's salvage capabilities for intact submarines will be limited to the Continental Shelf.

5.4. THE NAVY'S ROLE IN EDUCATION AND RESEARCH

Although the Navy's role in ocean science is separable and clearly mission-oriented, the Panel feels very strongly that it should continue to be closely linked with academic education and research. In the past this connection has been mutually profitable. Academic oceanography would hardly exist if the Navy, chiefly through the Office of Naval Research, had not provided leadership and imaginative support during the past 20 years. This is a debt universally and freely acknowledged by research oceanographers. On the Navy's side support of broad research has provided substantial information about oceans necessary to carry out its present mission. In addition many research tools developed for basic oceanography have served as prototypes for operationally useful equipment. Examples include explosive echo-ranging, the bathythermograph, deep-sea-moored buoys, deep submersibles, underwater photography, bottom profiling by precision depth-sounders and discovery of deep-scattering layers. Variable-depth sonar and short-pulse target identification were byproducts of oceanographic research. Moreover, oceanographers are highly responsive to Navy problems having little connection with research. Many instances can be cited of the Navy and the scientific community working hand in hand. Most recent of these is, of course, the concerted, successful effort to locate and recover the unarmed nuclear weapon off the Spanish coast. Response of the oceanographic community was instantaneous, and this group played a leading role in the weapon's recovery. In this instance, as in the tragic loss of Thresher, oceanographic institutions and civilian scientists put aside personal plans and volunteered to assist the Navy in its recovery mission. This civilian-Navy teamwork has proved highly successful and harmonious. Conversely, Navy personnel by virtue of their support of oceanographic laboratories are sufficiently aware of laboratory capabilities to facilitate immediate, effective action when an emergency arises.

Navy support of marine geophysical work in this country during the past decade has led to development of techniques for obtaining long-range sound transmission in oceans and acquisition of knowledge regarding parameters that affect it. When the Navy encounters difficulties with its sonar operations, competent people are available to rectify them. Similar instances in other fields of oceangraphy illustrate the interaction between civilian scientists and the Navy. Further, as the Navy's detection and weapon systems become more sophisticated this interaction can be expected to increase.

Finally, and vitally important, the Navy has been a major consumer of the output of academic oceanography in both manpower and science. Without increased numbers of scientists and engineers knowledgeable about oceans the Navy cannot carry out many of the programs reviewed above. Likewise, without the generalizations produced by academic research the Navy cannot efficiently utilize information collected to support these programs.

For these reasons the Panel strongly *recommends* that the Navy continue its support of academic research and education related to oceans. As was pointed out previously, the Navy's budget for oceanography has almost doubled in the fiscal years 1965–67 period. The Navy's contribution to academic oceanography in the area of basic research during the period has remained constant. Under these circumstances the Navy may not be able to effectively utilize oceanography in the future. It is important that the Navy maintain a proportionality between its support of academic research and education and its total oceanographic program. This would imply a marked increase in support of academic oceanography if the proportionality prior to 1965 is to be maintained as the whole Navy program expands.

We suggest, in addition that the ONR might profitably reexamine the particular importance of ocean science and technology to the Navy's basic mission.

5.5. INTERACTION OF NAVY PROGRAMS WITH CIVILIAN TECHNOLOGY

The Panel's projections concerning directions and rate of technological development discussed in section 4, upon which so much of the Nation's ocean program depends, assume that the Navy will successfully pursue its current projects on Deep Submergence Systems and Man in the Sea. In the event the Navy fails to accomplish its objectives in these areas the Panel's estimates of progress, time, and cost will have to be revised. In such case it would be in the Nation's interest to assign programs with similar goals to civilian agencies.

The recent successful location and recovery of the unarmed nuclear weapon off Spain demonstrated the mutual benefits of close Navy-industry cooperation. It is recommended that the Navy make a continuing, special effort to utilize the people, facilities, and know-how of the private sector in achieving its objectives in the Deep Submergence and Man in the Sea Projects. Only in this way can the Nation hope to capitalize quickly and profitably on its ocean technology capability. In the event complete information exchange would involve classified data, the Panel recommends that arrangements be made to provide properly qualified industrial groups with access to this classified information. By 1975 the Panel foresees the possibility of conducting complex, highly technical operations on the ocean bottom which are well beyond the limits of present technology. The Panel *recommends* that a proper Federal role related to ocean-technology development would be provision of a test range equipped with standardized stations in which component systems, concepts, and materials can be critically tested. Such a test range might consist of stations on the water's edge in the surf zone, at depths of 200, 600, 2,400, and 6,000 feet and perhaps in the abyssal deep. This facility would engender government-industry cooperation and technology developments with the desirable result of shortening the time required for specific developments and acceptance testing. The Navy in meeting its needs will undoubtedly require such a range. The Panel *recommends* that the Navy undertake a study which could lead to development of this range. Once implemented it should be made available to industrial and university groups, users, being expected to pay a prorated share of the total operating cost and depreciation, as is the case in other national facilities.

5.6. CONCLUSIONS

In section 5.2 an already extensive Navy dependence on oceanograph R & D was predicted to increase rapidly in the future. Not only are oceans becoming more important as arenas for strategic and tactical military operations, but operations themselves are pressing into less familiar or understood portions of the marine environment. The twofold growth of the Navy's oceanographic program over the fiscal year 1965-67 period, presented in section 5.3 testifies to the degree of recognition given by the Navy and Congress to increasing military need for knowledge of the marine environment and for carrying out service operations within it. This trend apparently will not be deemphasized in the future; if anything, the overall Navy oceanography program may accelerate.

The priorities which determine the bulk of the Navy's oceanographic efforts are primarily military, and certain of these considerations are paramount, involving specialized requirements for both research and surveys, as well as engineering developments. We therefore *recommend* that the program remain solely under Navy direction rather than consolidated with perhaps somewhat similar programs of other agencies such as ESSA or a new civilian agency of ocean development such as the one proposed in this report (see sec. 10.4).

Support figures discussed in section 5.3 indicate that basic research has remained relatively constant while the overall Navy oceanography program has approximately doubled. It is not entirely clear to us that the great increase in ocean-engineering effort associated with such new programs as the Deep Submergence Systems Project should proceed indefinitely without a corresponding increase in the Navy's basic-research support. A proportionality between research, particularly basic research, and the total R & D effort in the given fields should probably be maintained if brute-force engineering solutions are not to be inadvertently substituted for what ought to be more discriminating deployment of operational requirements made possible by greater environmental knowledge. Such knowledge generally requires considerable lead time for development and a long-term investment attitude toward research programs that produce it. It is in this connection that we wish to emphasize the importance of strengthening the traditional Navy tie with the oceanographic research and educational community, which appears to be jeopardized at present by stronger bonds with industry. Prompt and effective assistance from the ocean-science community to such urgent needs as the Thresher search and the recent successful weapon-recovery operation off Spain are, we feel, dramatic and by no means isolated examples of the beneficial, responsive nature of this tie. Both direct evidence from budgets and indirect evidence from excellent research proposals for basic studies which have been refused suggest the need for increased Navy support of the basic oceanographic sciences and technologies.

6.0. Opportunities in Oceanographic Research

6.1. OBSERVATION

Until recently oceanographic observations could be characterized as being *exploratory* in nature. Expeditions were undertaken, usually with a single ship, to survey unknown regions or to observe special phenomena discovered on an earlier expedition. Exploratory surveys have frequently provided new information which has been useful in *asking* questions of critical scientific importance but not so often in *answering* them. Another consequence of the emphasis given to exploratory observation is that oceanographers have been physically and intellectually isolated from their colleagues in basic disciplines and in other geophysical sciences.

In recent years exploratory observations, although they still dominate oceanography, have begun to yield to more systematic observations designed for specific purposes. There are a number of reasons for this change.

First, there is a growing awareness that the most challenging scientific problems encompass two or more of the environmental sciences. For example, oceanic circulation cannot be understood apart from atmospheric circulation, nor can atmospheric circulation be predicted for periods of more than a few days without considering the ocean. Development of a theory of climate will require treating the oceans and atmosphere as a thoroughly interacting system. The complexities of the interactions are illustrated by the processes of sedimentation on the bottom of the sea. These processes are governed by physical and biological conditions within the volume of the oceans, which depend on the interaction of the oceans and the atmosphere.

Second, new platforms and sensors are becoming available which permit new observations. Acoustic and electromagnetic probes make possible remote sensing, "swallow" floats give unequivocal records of subsurface currents, thermistor chains can furnish continuous records of temperature distribution and "hot wires" provide information about the turbulent spectrum. Many other examples could be cited.

Third, developments in data processing and in methods of data analysis represent major advances. Telemetering techniques provide vast quantities of data far beyond that available a decade ago, and the newer computers permit systematic analysis of these data and facilitate study of matematical models by integration of governing differential equations. A consequence of these new capabilities in data processing and analysis is that quantitative determinations are beginning to replace qualitative and intuitive accounts which characterized geophysical sciences a few years ago. For example, direct measurement of vertical flux and wind stress can now be made by spectral analysis of fluctuations. New insights into the mechanism of nonlinear coupling, made possible by computer technology, have contributed significantly to theories of wave generation and motions of a variety of scales.

These developments in observational techniques, data processing, and interpretation have proved to be equally valuable in studies of the oceans, atmosphere, and solid earth. A strong coupling of research among various fields of geophysics exists. There is a basic commonality in observational platforms, techniques of analysis and underlying theory. A fruitful idea in one field is likely to be equally profitable in other geophysical fields. Thus, broadly trained, creative scientists may provide crucial leadership in several fields simultaneously.

A close connection also exists between geophysical and biological problems, despite the fact that these connections have often been overlooked. Certain regions owe their great biological productivity to subtle combinations of chemical and physical processes which vitally need to be understood. Oceanographers are well aware of the importance of these relationships, and in the future we see a closer relationship between biological and physical studies of the sea. This will be especially important as modification of the environment becomes more widespread (see sec. 3).

Our new abilities to observe and interpret the environment have brought within the range of reasonable possibility a number of major scientific and technological enterprises. These require increased understanding of the functioning of systems far more complex than those which can be studied in the laboratory. Consequently, there are of the highest intrinsic scientific interest, as well as of great practical importance.

6.2. PREDICTION

We are in the very early stages of developing the capability for ocean prediction. Until World War II ocean predictions were limited to truly periodic phenomena whose mechanism was clearly understood—tides and seasons. Tidal predictions are still imperfect, and improvements based on more complete treatment of nonlinear effects and transients associated with surface winds and pressure are within reach.

In the past two decades methods have been devised for:

(a) Prediction of surface waves based on observations and predictions of surface-wind distribution.

(b) Warnings of tsunamis produced by earthquakes which are readily detected at great distances.

These methods have proved vital for safety and economy in coastal areas, in commercial shipping and for many military operations. Further improvement in wave prediction is tied closely to atmospheric prediction, for which atmospheric observations over the oceans are required. In a similar way prediction of the depth of the surface mixed layer, still in its early stages, is closely tied to the meteorological problem. Understanding the processes occurring in the surface mixed layer is important for acoustic-transmission applications within the sea and for marine biological problems.

We have reason to think that these phenomena, for which rather simple prediction methods are available, fail to encompass other characteristic, important features of the ocean. From the fragmentary evidence we have at present, it appears that a wide range of time-dependent phenomena do indeed occur in the ocean, as our experience with stratified fluids in the laboratory or in the atmosphere would lead us to expect. Ocean weather may be as varied and complex as the weather in the atmosphere. For example, we see indications of internal gravity waves, inertial motions associated with the earth's rotation, turbulence, meanders in the Gulf Stream and other currents and fluctuations in surface temperature over large areas; but we have not yet adequately described any of these phenomena. Whether current systems occur which are comparable in size to atmospheric planetary waves remains to be discovered. The extent to which prediction of these phenomena is inherently feasible and for what scales of time and space remains unknown; these problems appear destined to become some of the most exciting objectives of ocean research in the next decade. The answers are not obvious, for although the governing differential equations are well known, we do not know the strength of coupling between observable and unobservable scales.

We do know, however, that lack of ocean surface-layer observations restricts effective atmospheric prediction to a few days.

Until the prediction problem is better understood, the potentialities of deliberate ocean modification cannot be determined. Without such understanding, large-scale experiments addressed to diverting ocean currents, to melting the Arctic ice or to overturning large regions of ocean water would be extravagant and highly irresponsible. However, inadvertent modification of coastal areas, already of local concern, is likely to become more serious. In order to plan wisely for use and development of coastal areas we must learn to predict such effects as increased pollution, changes in coastlines, and deepening of harbors.

Finally, a remark should be made concerning the space and scale of ocean observations envisioned by this Panel. For the present and for the foreseeable future ocean observations should be undertaken as research and development programs, with specifications closely linked to objectives and with results linked to subsequent planning. The first stages should be distinctly limited in scope and in areal extent; but one should anticipate observational systems covering very large areas. It will be necessary to establish and maintain numbers of observing platforms in, on and above the sea. Reliable communication systems of considerable complexity will be needed. Furthermore, the inherently global nature of many scientific problems will require support of research on a larger scale and more stable basis than has been the case heretofore.

6.3. PHYSICAL PROCESSES

A catalog on research problems in physical oceanography captures neither the flavor nor the intellectual quality of scientific challenges posed by the oceans. For example in the ocean bottom a well-documented history of our planet is recorded, perhaps containing far more information about the early stages of evolution of our planet and the solar system than on the moon's scarred surface. The oceans are a giant laboratory for fluid dynamics, which illustrates the full complexity of hydrodynamics. The oceans, in turn, interact with both the solid earth and atmosphere in direct and subtle ways, and one can never hope to gain a comprehensive understanding from study limited to the oceans themselves.

We will not compose a detailed framework of oceanographic research nor catalog the variety of work in progress at existing institutions.[1] Instead, we will concentrate upon defining specific, new types of large-scale projects not yet underway which seem to offer great potential for increased knowledge. The emphasis on *large-scale* projects in this section does not imply that progress in oceanography can be achieved only in this way. The large-scale projects originate through the efforts of individual researchers seeking answers to problems posed by theoretical, laboratory of small-scale observational studies.

Benthic Boundary. At the bottom of the deep ocean there is a transition from fluid, to fluid with suspended particles, to solid with interstitial fluid, to solid. The detailed nature of this boundary is unknown, as well as whether its characteristics result primarily from physical or biological processes. An understanding of this boundary

---

[1] Chapter II, "National Academy of Sciences' Committee on Oceanography Report" (in preparation), provides one account of such background material.

44

is essential in order to solve such problems as long-range sound transmission of powerful sonars (SQS–26), occupation at the bottom in permanent or semipermanent structures and search for objects at or near the bottom. The study of the benthic boundary is now possible because of the development of recording devices and probes which measure temperature, velocity, and pressure fluctuations at great depths.

The benthic boundary is a base for studying the earth below. Beneath the oceans the earth's crust is thin, and environmental conditions for measurement are quiet. A recent surprising discovery is that standard geophysical methods of exploration (seismic, gravimetric, magnetic, and geothermal) yield better results than on land. The greater technical difficulties of working on the sea bottom are more than compensated by advantages of a uniform environment. There remains, of course, great ambiguity about the deeper material. This can only be resolved by coring the sediments (JOIDES) and the layer beneath (MOHOLE).

An opportunity exists for adapting other geophysical techniques developed on land for marine use. For example, measurements on the sea bottom of the fluctuating electric and magnetic fields at various frequencies could provide information about the variation of conductivity with depth; from this, one can, in principle infer internal temperature and ultimately horizontal stresses between oceans and continents. Our understanding of mountain making and of the very existence of oceans and continents depends on assessment of stresses at the margin of basins.

It is now possible to make deep-ocean tide measurements from instruments lowered to the seabed. Theories of the origin of the moon depend critically on the efficacy of tides in disposing of the mechanical energy of the earth-moon system. Do tides in the solid earth slow down the earth's rotation and move the moon outward or are the ocean tides responsible? Additional tidal measurements on a global scale are required in order to settle the problem.

Further understanding of the benthic boundary depends on continued development of instruments operable at great depths. Many observational programs require data-collection over long periods of time, and substantial technological problems exist in collecting these data. Furthermore, the ocean bottom is not uniform, and isolated observations are unlikely to yield a proper view. We can thus expect continuing expansion of measurements on a global scale. The opportunity exists for perhaps solving an important cosmological problem, and we *recommend* that tidal measurements be made for many parts of the oceans to determine once and for all the nature and magnitude of oceanic tidal friction.

The Abyssal Ocean. The deep distribution of oceanic variables (temperature, salinity, current, etc.), and planktonic and sedimentary particles appears to be determined by upwelling and turbulent fluxes. The most urgent need is for observational studies of the turbulent mixing processes. A thorough, well-planned effort to study the turbulent microstructure of the main thermocline would provide insight on the general circulation of the oceans, global weather and climatic fluctuations as well. It is intolerable that direct measurements of turbulent fluxes at depth are not being attempted. In our judgment this is within present-day technological capability but might require substantial engineering. A few pioneering studies made with sensors mounted on submarines and lowered by wire from surface vessels have shown fascinating microstructure. These studies provide a good basis for future development. Submarines are essential to the study of water under ice sheets. This cold water, of high salinity and density, eventually becomes the water at the greatest depths. The development of the bottom water remains largely unknown.

Distinction between various modes and types of internal waves and what is ineptly referred to as turbulence has to be clarified. Perhaps, most random variation of temperature currents can be associated with internal, gravity-inertial and planetary waves. Distribution of energy among different modes, frequencies, and directions needs disentanglement. The existence of an equatorial, internal wave trap between 30° S. and 30° N. lends interest to a geographical study of these distributions. Nonlinear interactions among these modes (including "general circulation" as zero frequency mode) and the irregular sea bottom need to be studied theoretically and experimentally. It is here that a solution to the problem of dynamic oceanography may be sought. We must cease to be surprised at irregularity of oscillations whenever appropriate observations are made. Irregularity is expected as a consequence of the fact that 10^{20} ergs sec^{-1} of energy are dissipated in the ocean, and this calls for r.m.s. (root mean square) shear of 10^{-1} sec^{-1}.

Buoy Programs. During the past few years several draft plans have been submitted to international bodies for oceanwide observational programs employing dozens of ships extending over several years—purportedly to study variability of oceanic circulation. To us they have seemed ill-designed from the point of view of sampling, because we believe it would be better to study smaller scales and higher frequencies first, even though these do not provide busywork for fleets of oceanographic vessels. In fact instrumented buoys seem better adapted to variability studies, although ships will, of course, be necessary to service them.

To date, use of moored buoys has been largely limited to efforts of individuals who, lacking the resources, logistic support, and necessary organization, have been unable to maintain dense enough arrays for a long enough time to gather statistically significant data. The signals are complex, and a sophisticated measuring program is required to read them. The problem would be difficult enough if all oceanic fluctuations were a broad spectrum of linearly superimposed internal waves, but, as mentioned above, there is undoubtedly a significantly nonlinear domain. Oceanographers need to evolve some fairly elaborate measuring arrays, with limited regions heavily instrumented. They are in the position of radio astronomers who need a radio telescope of a novel design, a facility quite beyond the capability of a single individual to design, build, and operate. The oceanographic community has been too concerned with conventional research and fund-raising and has devoted insufficient attention to exciting new scientific projects such as a viable buoy program.

A graduated program for measuring and identifying regular oscillations in a typical deep-sea area is described in appendix II. This is one of several proposals which have emerged in the last few months from groups interested in buoy programs.

Air-Sea Boundary. In order to predict large-scale atmospheric behavior for periods longer than a day or two, vertical fluxes of heat, momentum, and water vapor must be specified at the surface, both on land and in sea. Research and development along several independent lines are needed.

The spectral structure of atmospheric turbulence is being determined, and direct measurements of vertical fluxes are being made with rapidly responding sensors mounted on fixed platforms, aircraft, or submarines. Temperature and wind velocity sensors exist in experimental form. Interesting work is under way at a few institutions, but adequate humidity sensors have yet to be developed. This lack represents an important constraint on air-sea interaction research. Mean profiles measured from fixed platforms and buoys are also being used at a few institutions to estimate vertical fluxes.

However, in order to relate vertical flux measured at a point by either of the above methods to the "synoptic" scale commensurate with the weather prediction problem, measurements using integral methods over extended areas are needed. These require a carefully planned and coordinated program of research utilizing fixed platforms, buoys, aircraft, and possibly submarines. To date such programs have not been initiated.

Methods of isotopic and surface chemistry have recently been applied to the air-sea boundary, and these offer some interesting opportunities which should be exploited.

A substantial effort has been directed to the study of surface waves, particularly with regard to nonlinear actions and generation by wind. Studies have been dominantly theoretical; the need is for adequate field and laboratory measurements. Recent measurements of wave growth seriously differ from the accepted theory of wave generation. A substantial improvement could be achieved by means of a larger array of bottom-mounted pressure sensors (wave telescopes) which monitor the surface-trapped energy with reasonable resolution.

Coastal Boundary. The focus of the intersection of the surface and bottom boundary is the coastal zone. The hydrodynamics of breaking waves, tides, and tsunamis on the sloping shelf is not clearly understood. The mechanism of interaction between moving fluid and sediment underneath is not at all understood. It is well known that coastal structures do not perform in a way that is expected in other engineering fields. There are many examples of marinas where the annual dredging cost equals the construction cost, or harbors where sheltering breakwaters have led to increased seiching or wave action within the harbor. This points to the subject's difficulty, the need for fundamental research, and better application of known rules to actual practice.

The Individual Scientist's Role. Hydrodynamic studies of the oceans and atmosphere have fused with similar geophysical and astrophysical areas in recent years, forming a new arena of intellectual activity called "geophysical fluid dynamics." Although originally oriented toward theoretical aspects, there has been an increasing tendency to develop laboratory experiments and field observations. In theoretical work and laboratory investigations efforts are largely individual, the goal being to formulate and solve problems in fluid mechanics which have bearing on basic understanding of the oceans. The geophysical fluid dynamics group focuses on exchanging ideas and maintaining enthusiasm at a high level of creative, individual activity. From these individual scientists come most of the ideas which are translated into questions about the oceans, which, in turn, motivate larger, organized data-collecting projects mentioned above. For example, the suggestion of an internal wave trap about the equator resulted from pioneer investigations of the motion of fluids on a rotating sphere. Conversely, results of the observational projects react on theoretical work so that it proceeds soundly. Our reason for mentioning the role of these individuals is to emphasize how essential they are and to insure that this effort is not overlooked in the hurly-burly of larger plans.

Summary. It appears to us that it is now appropriate to end an era in which the main emphasis within physical oceanography has been on exploration. The MOHOLE and JOIDES programs to core far below the sea floor at carefully selected sites are more reasonable for the present level of oceanography. Likewise, the new, developing technology of bottom-mounted and buoy-supported instruments coupled with theoretical advances derived from efforts in geophysical fluid dynamics should lead to substantial, new, observational programs. These programs, as outlined above, can provide information about the environment essential for living sensibly within the oceans and using them. The focus should be on the nature of the benthic boundary, the weather and climate of deep oceans, and the interaction of oceans with the atmosphere and the coast.

6.4. BIOLOGICAL PROCESSES

The subpanel on marine biology has surveyed the major areas of current biological research through discussions with Federal agency representatives, visits to selected laboratories and discussions with biologists. Although some of the major problems of marine biology have been considered in previous reports,[2] the Panel believes that there are three areas of research to which insufficient attention has been given. These concern new approaches to obtaining more food from the sea (see sec. 2), use of marine organisms in biomedical research, and problems associated with large-scale environmental modifications (see sec. 3). The latter problem is illustrated currently by the possibility that a sea-level canal will be constructed across the Isthmus of Panama.

The Panel believes that marine biology must be regarded in broad terms. Specifically, marine biology embraces four major areas of research:

1. Animal and plant populations and their interaction with each other and the ocean.

2. The unique characteristics of diverse marine organisms that enable them to survive in the ocean.

3. Utilization of marine organisms as unique experimental material for investigation of biomedical problems.

4. The processes and factors involved in food production from the sea.

Some of the most scientifically interesting and socially significant problems confronting mankind exist in this arena.

Populations in the Sea. The conversion of photosynthetic plants to animal protein on land is relatively well understood. In the sea, however, photosynthetic plants are restricted largely to microscopic planktonic algae (phytoplankton); conversion to animals large enough to serve as food for man usually involves many intermediate steps.

---

[2] Chapter II, "National Academy of Sciences' Committee on Oceanography Report" (in preparation); "National Oceanographic Program Fiscal Year 1967," ICO Pamphlet No. 24, March 1966; "A Report to the Division of Biological and Medical Sciences of the National Science Foundation" by the *ad hoc* Committee on Biological Oceanography; "A Scientific Framework for the Study of the World's Oceans," UNESCO.

Our knowledge of the complex and diverse food chains and food webs of the sea is very sparse. The natural foods of even the best-known marine animal species are unknown except in general terms. Central and prerequisite to scientific control and ultimate management of marine food resources is further knowledge of essential nutritional requirements, of feeding habits and food preferences, and of efficiency in converting planktonic algae to animal protein.

Plants and Photosynthesis. Photosynthetic plants in the sea and on land use solar energy to synthesize organic matter from inorganic materials. In agriculture, solar energy is channeled into production of plants that are useful to mankind, either directly as plant products or indirectly as animal food. Growth of plants in the sea, on the other hand, is a process over which we have no control and little knowledge. Some species of planktonic algae are recognized as food organisms for marine animals; others are "weed" species of little or no nutritional value; still others, such as "red tide" organisms, are noxious or lethal to marine life. To increase significantly the amount of food obtained from the sea, we must learn to control the kinds of phytoplankton produced as the primary food source. Expanded and intensified programs in marine microbiology in its broadest sense, including both laboratory and field studies, are needed to provide fundamental background and practical experience.

Environmental Studies. Although human intervention is increasingly affecting natural populations of organisms, very little is known about environmental conditions that govern these populations in nature. Without adequate knowledge it is difficult to predict the effects of human intervention or to define proper procedures for management and exploitation. The complexity of the marine environment has limited the rate of progress in understanding (see sec. 3).

Comprehensive studies are needed for insight into the complex relationships of organisms to their environment. These must be sufficiently long-term to permit measurements of fluctuations in the meaningful parameters and the resultant changes that occur naturally. Included should be intensive studies of carefully selected habitat types with surveys of related habitats to indicate variability. Most importantly, there should be constant interplay between observation and analysis of the natural situation by experimental alteration of biological, physical, and chemical properties of the environment and by laboratory experimentation under controlled conditions on a sufficiently large scale to provide an adequate model of the natural habitat. The requisite research groups should include scientists who are knowledgeable about the physical and chemical properties of the environment and those specifically competent in the physiology and behavior of organisms.

50

It is evident from studies of organisms in fresh-water environments that the difficulties in understanding the complex relationships and interactions among organisms are compounded by lumping species together as plant producers, herbivores, and carnivores. There is a need for precise identification of each species, rare as well as abundant. Abundant species may account for most food production, but rare ones often provide essential services, such as parasite removal, to other species. Eliminating these services may be catastrophic. In addition, cryptic species may be present which, while not differing appreciably in morphology, have quite different behavioral, physiological and population characteristics in the environment.

Consideration of the function of individual species in the environment brings into prominence the present shortage of systematists who define species, suggest evolutionary relationships, and identify distinguishing characteristics of organisms. There is great need of comprehensive study of the systematic, taxonomic biology of marine organisms involving morphological, biochemical, and behavioral differences among species. Such studies provide a basis for selecting races or strains, within a single species, with characteristics which render them particularly appropriate for exploitation and cultivation by man. Characteristics of interest are rapid growth, adaptability to culture conditions and resistance to disease.

If a sea-level canal is opened across Central America, many biological problems of great potential consequence will emerge. A number of species have close relatives on opposite sides of the present land mass which has existed for 80 million years. These closely related species show different amounts of divergence. What will happen if the barrier is breached so that organisms can move between oceans through such a canal? Will changing selection pressures and competition eliminate species? Will closely related species interbreed and form a hybrid population or remain separate with, perhaps, accompany changes in their genetic, physiological, behavioral, and population characteristics? Will present populations resist invasions unchanged, or will serious disruptions occur, accompanied by violent oscillations in the composition and abundance of species?

Knowledge of characteristics of both successful and unsuccessful invading species should help us predict the effects of purposeful introduction or removal of species elsewhere. Some changes are likely to be dramatic and easily documented; others will be more subtle although of equal importance in furthering our understanding. It will be impossible to recognize and understand these subtle changes unless the present state of populations of various species is known thoroughly. In view of the immediate need for background information, the Panel recommends undertaking an intensive study of marine organisms on both sides of the proposed canal site. Concurrently, for purposes of comparison and generalization, planktonic and benthic organisms in the adjacent deep seas and in waters on the continental shelves should also be studied intensively.

Unique Characteristics of Marine Organisms. Existence and behavior of marine organisms in specific habitats depend on unique physiological characteristics which deserve investigation in their own right. For example, organisms deep in the oceans live under extraordinarily constant and extreme conditions. In the deepest areas, pressures are more than 500 atmospheres, temperatures are less than 4° C. and darkness is total except for occasional flashes of light produced by luminescent organisms. The environment is unlike anything encountered elsewhere in the solar system. Investigation of organisms adapted to live under such extreme conditions, though difficult and requiring special laboratory facilities, may provide new insights into man's basic metabolic processes and physiological mechanisms.

Biomedical Applications. Our present understanding of many biomedical problems is based largely upon research initially conducted on lower organisms. The insights so afforded are valid because many biological processes of most kinds of organisms are fundamentally alike. Understanding of mammalian genetics stems in part from research on insects and micro-organisms; our understanding of human biochemistry derives from studies of lower animals and plants; and many of our present insights into the phenomena of fertilization and embryonic development are derived primarily from investigations of marine organisms.

One of the most challenging areas of contemporary biological research concerns growth and development. We still know little about how a human egg, one cell, is transformed into an adult composed of billions of cells in a thousand varieties, all precisely organized to produce a normally functioning individual. When normal development goes awry, various abnormalities or birth defects result. Much of our knowledge of fertilization and development has been obtained from studying marine organisms, some of which develop from egg to adult in 1 day and during this time are open to continuous observation and experimental manipulation. Study of the development of diverse marine organisms remains the best opportunity for enhancing our understanding of developmental biology.

Other general biochemical and physiological processes have also been investigated effectively with marine organisms. The use of squid axons to study conduction in nerves is a dramatic example. Our knowledge of the structure and function of sensory receptors and the significance of neurosecretion have also been enriched greatly through use of marine organisms.

52

With the conquest of many infectious diseases, the degenerative diseases of old age have become increasingly important and research on the aging process is rapidly becoming more sophisticated. Because some marine organisms reach old age in a few hours, whereas others have long lifespans or reproduce asexually and hence are virtually immortal, marine organisms are valuable for studies on the processes of aging in nature.

The value of biochemical studies on the great diversity of marine plants and animals is indicated by the isolation of chemicals that have antiviral, antimicrobial, cancer-inhibiting, nerve-blocking, or heart-stimulating properties in laboratory experiments. Some of these chemicals have potential pharmacological value, as shown by biotoxins from poisonous shellfish and pufferfish that are 200,000 times more powerful in blocking nervous activity than drugs such as curare presently used for this purpose. Such powerful chemicals are obviously important tools for neurologists who are elucidating biochemical events responsible for nerve and brain activity, and offer promise of application as useful drugs.

The number of chemicals that may be found by intensive analysis of marine organisms is well illustrated by recent studies on sponges, one of the most primitive animals. Sponges produce at least 15 different types of sterols not found in higher animals, including man. By studying unusual sterols in sponges, we may acquire a better understanding of the role of related sterols in man. In addition, investigations of sponges unexpectedly revealed a unique material, an arabinosyl nucleoside, which may have practical importance in that it is apparently highly effective in treatment of certain virus infections and leukemia in laboratory animals. Other products from sponges also show a broad spectrum of antimicrobial effects.

Many sea cucumbers, starfish, and their relatives produce highly toxic mixtures of steroid glycosides, a group of chemicals that includes the powerful cardiac drug, digitalis, which is obtained from a terrestrial plant. Steroid glycosides from these marine organisms have suppressed growth of several different kinds of tumor in experimental animals and may provide leads toward the chemotherapy of malignant tumors.

The list of pharmacologically active substances extracted from marine organisms is expanding as more investigators enter this virtually untapped field of research in natural products. With development of biochemical analyses and refined techniques for cultivating many marine organisms that produce chemicals which may prove to be of medical importance, the time is now ripe for intensified research in marine biochemistry and pharmacology. Drugs are now derived primarily from terrestrial plants and bacteria or are synthesized in the laboratory. The great variety of plant and animal life in the sea offers abundant opportunities for study in many areas of bio medical research.

The results cited above have resulted mainly from individual research. There is an obvious need for larger scale projects, but it is clear that advances in marine biology will always depend heavily on individual research. It is, therefore, essential that support for these scientists be continued and increased.

In summary, the situation with respect to marine biology parallels that of physical oceanography. There are many clearly identifiable problems. Although there remains a need for special ocean surveys, we no longer need to give special emphasis to them. The broad outlines of the subject are clear. What is needed is a much greater emphasis on the problem areas reviewed above.

7.0. Economic Aspects of Oceanography

7.1. INTRODUCTION

.An ideal economic evaluation of oceanographic research and development would compare the future performance of an economy with and without different levels of expenditure for oceanographic programs. It would emphasize that the value of the oceanography is likely to be crucially dependent upon concurrent technological, demographic, and economic developments. Moreover, it would determine the value of the programs only after due consideration of their interactions with other existing and potential economic activities. For example, an investment in oceanography might find deposits of low-grade nickel ore on the sea floor. However, the same investment might also find similar ores on land. Likewise, developments in metallurgy might substantially reduce requirements for nickel in alloys of steel and thereby make all but the highest grade ores on land uneconomical to mine. These are rather simple alternatives. Analysis may become much more complex if such problems as the strength of the merchant marine or the drain on gold reserves enter into consideration. Finally, the analysis becomes much more uncertain as the time between expenditure and potential benefit increases.

Consequently, a really effective model for evaluating oceanographic programs is almost certainly beyond the state of the art. We are reduced to accepting the usual alternative used by economists when evaluating large Government programs; namely, partial analysis on a project-by-project basis. The validity of this approach usually depends crucially on the assumption that certain interactions between the program and other economic activities are relatively unimportant. The technique is widely used in the Defense Department but the planning horizon is usually only 5 years and the application usually has been to develop the optimum means for achieving a fairly well-defined objective. Thus, this application is considerably simpler than an analysis of the potential economic benefits of oceanographic research and development programs which has neither agreed objectives nor a definite time limit.

Nevertheless, an attempt to apply project-by-project analysis to oceanography exists.[1] It is imaginative and pioneering, but can be criticized on several grounds:

1. An inadequate distinction between gross and net benefits;
2. A casual approach to estimation of future demands and benefits;
3. The assumption that the future benefits from different investments will not vary too irregularly over time;
4. An incomplete effort to estimate the probable effect of other changes in technology and economic preferences on benefits derivable from the oceanographic program; and
5. A failure in some instances to distinguish whether the relevant area or economy over which benefits are to be calculated is national or international.

The application of benefit-cost analysis to oceanographic *research* (as differentiated from oceanographic programs) is also of uncertain value. There is considerable evidence that most Government-sponsored research is supported because it contributes to certain national objectives. Thus, oceanographic research, as such, probably should be construed as an overhead, staff or support activity for achieving national objectives related to the ocean. Consequently, it is not particularly fruitful to evaluate the *specific* benefit of *individual* research efforts in oceanography, because they are rarely directly identified with any particular mission.

For oceanography, and apparently many other research activities as well, two levels of research support seem to exist: The first tier includes research activities undertaken quite directly by an agency assigned with a specific operating responsibility; the second relates to a more general level of research support with benefits accruing to a broad group of missions. National Science Foundation support seems more akin to the second type. By contrast, many research activities conducted within and directly under the control of an operating agency with specific missions are fairly attributed directly to those missions.

---

[1] "Economic Benefits from Oceanographic Research," National Academy of Sciences, National Research Council (Publ. 1228), 1964. This is referred to in this section as the NASCO Report.[2]

[2] For a critical evaluation of the NASCO Report, "Economic Benefits," see below and James A. Crutchfield, Robert W. Kates, and W. R. Derrick Sewell, "Benefit-Cost Analysis and the National Oceanographic Program," to be published in the *Journal of Natural Resources*, October 1966.

7.2. AN ECONOMIC EVALUATION OF THE OCEANOGRAPHIC PROGRAM

The objectives or missions of the national oceanographic program may be placed under six headings.[3]

1. Improved environmental prediction and modification;
2. Aiding development of new sources of raw materials for industrial use;
3. Furthering the more complete exploitation of biological resources represented by marine life, ranging from improved fisheries' yields to biomedical applications;
4. Improvement of near-oceanographic environment by finding more expeditious and less costly means to preserve, modify, or reduce pollution of estuaries, beaches, and other coastal waters;
5. Improvement in ocean navigation, ship design, and ports;
6. National defense.

At the present, allocation of national oceanographic program funds to these missions (other than defense, which is treated separately elsewhere in this report) appears to be roughly as shown in table 7.1. These figures do *not* include approximately $14 to $15 million of general or second tier nondefense research support not directly related to a mission. For the most part, this second tier research is conducted at academic institutions or similar facilities and is funded by NSF.

By way of comparison, NASCO estimates of the discounted annual value of average benefits to be realized from civilian missions of the national oceanographic program are presented in table 7.2. It should be stressed that these numbers are reported only to lend perspective. There are many reasons for suspecting these estimates.[4] Furthermore, the costs reported in table 7.1 are *not* directly comparable to benefits reported in table 7.2, since realization of estimated benefits would depend upon additional investments or outlays being undertaken elsewhere by the government or in the private sector of the economy to complement these programs. For example, environmental objectives would almost surely need to be complemented by Weather Bureau activities (which now require an expenditure of well over $100

---

[3] These mission definitions were adapted from the NAS/NRC report, "Economic Benefits From Oceanographic Research." Much of the structure of the following discussion results from accepting these definitions to facilitate comparisons.

[4] For documentation of this point see Crutchfield, et al.

million annually) while exploitation of raw materials in the sea would require considerably more than expenditures on oceanography alone. In short, benefits reported in table 7.2 are gross benefits that might be expected from the national oceanographic program taken in conjunction with a range of private and public expenditures elsewhere in the economy. These gross benefits could be used to derive a meaningful net present value or benefit/cost ratio only with an estimate of *all* investment and operating costs, both public and private, of achieving these benefits.

TABLE 7.1.—*Estimated oceanographic nondefense expenditures on major U.S. Government missions related to the ocean or environmental improvement,* * fiscal year 1967*

[In millions of dollars]

Improved environmental prediction and modification	14. 5
Development of new sources of raw materials for use in industry	12. 0
Improved exploitation of marine biological resources (mainly fisheries)	45. 0
Improvement of the near oceanographic environment	10. 5
Improvement in ocean navigation, etc	38. 0
Total	120. 0

*These numbers differ from those listed by ICO for the national ocean program. The Panel believes that this table more adequately describes the total level of activity.

TABLE 7.2.—*NASCO estimates of the discounted annual value of average benefits of the civilian missions of the National Oceanographic Program*

Mission:	Million dollars per year
Improved environmental prediction and modification (mainly better weather forecasting)	600
Development of new sources of raw materials for use in industry	105
Improved exploitation of marine biological resources (U.S.-owned fisheries only)	414
Improvement of near oceanographic environment (including cost reductions in sewage disposal)	629
Improvement in ocean navigation, etc. (U.S. shipping only)	365

Moreover, the benefit figures reported in table 7.2 are somewhat tenuous. For example, the major expected benefits from improved weather forecasting listed in the NASCO report are as follows (on an annual basis, undiscounted):

	Millions
Reduced flood damage	$280
Increased efficiency in scheduling labor and equipment in the construction industry	1, 000
Savings from better scheduling coal, oil and natural gas production, oil refining, and transportation	500

Improved planning and scheduling of commercial vegetable, potato, and
fruit production : [1]   *Millions*
    On the farm only_____ $185
    Including processing and marketing cost_____ 185
Better planning of cattle and hog production_____ 450
                                                                     _____
        Total_____ 2, 600

[1] The $370,000,000 figure reported here for savings on commercial vegetables, potato, and fruit production is to be contrasted with the $500,000,000 reported in NASCO's report. The $370,000,000 figure was derived by reworking basic numbers NASCO reported and applying their percentages to derive savings. It is not clear exactly how they derived the $500,000,000 estimate, but it was more than compensated by rounding their total to $2,000,000,000.

An interaction problem immediately arises with regard to the flood control estimates; clearly, if NASCO estimates are correct and the oceanography program NASCO projects are adopted, Corps of Engineers' estimates on savings to be obtained from flood control installations should be adjusted downward in some cases. Furthermore, for an estimate of the net social benefit to the economy, it would have to be assumed that increments to the flood control program planned by the Corps of Engineers over the next few years that could be expected to yield or duplicate identical benefits would be eliminated from Corps of Engineers' budgets; whether or not this elimination would occur would depend, of course, upon a number of uncertainties, some of a political nature. It is also possible that the Corps of Engineers' program would be a cheaper solution to flood control than an oceanographic program. Indeed in all probability the optimal or lower cost solution involves some of both programs.

Similar detailed criticisms could be made with regard to other estimated savings. Given these conflicting considerations, it is very difficult to say what actual savings would result from improvements on long-range weather forecasting. With conservatism, the $2 billion annual estimate reported by NASCO, might be reduced to one-half billion annually undiscounted or approximately $150 million on a discounted average annual basis. The important point is that even this very conservative figure is quite large compared to the present annual outlay of $14.5 million on oceanographic efforts in weather forecasting. Of course, this is only part of the Government's effort to improve weather forecasts or environmental control. Still, potential gains seem large enough to justify at least the present expenditure and probably to justify an increase.

A somewhat more cautious conclusion seems warranted for Government-oceanographic expenditures except for surveys and other conventional services, aimed at developing new sources of raw materials.

The mining and petroleum industries have shown a considerable willingness to invest in the development of ocean or any other resources wherever commercial prospects appear reasonably good. These industries, with their considerable commitment and experience, are very well situated to evaluate the relative economic attractiveness of different sources of raw materials, including those under water. Thus, development of ocean raw materials is now subject to a market test that seems to be yielding reasonably sensible answers. Before any substantial Government involvement is advocated, proof should be rendered that private companies now involved have been grossly ineffective or socially irresponsible in exploiting oceanic raw materials (see secs. 4.11 and 10.2).

The level of expenditure required to provide survey and similar aids for ocean development on a scale commensurate with that traditionally available on land depends on new technological developments, some of which might become available as a byproduct of national defense programs. It has been estimated that an expenditure of approximately $50 to $100 million over the next 10 years on development of new survey equipment and instrumentation would eliminate major obstacles to obtaining efficient topographic and geological surveys of the U.S. continental shelves (see sec. 4.6). Even with better equipment, however, some upward drift in survey expenditures from the present level of $12 million might be needed and justified for these purposes.

With regard to better exploitation of marine biological resources, the NASCO report places a very heavy emphasis on improving the position of the U.S. fishing industry. Superficially, it would seem very difficult to confine improvement in fishery yields to the U.S. industry as such. Improvements from oceanographic research that help the U.S. fishing industry would likely improve the position of fishing industries abroad as well. Indeed, present performance suggests that foreign fleets would be quicker than U.S. industry to adopt new techniques.[5] The fact that several less-developed countries tend to have relatively substantial fishing industries further strengthens the argument. The dubious character of national distinctions in these matters is only heightened by the fact that U.S. industry is increasingly investing in fishing activities conducted under other national flags. Therefore, to the extent that improvement in oceanographic knowledge would lead to increased production in fishery industries of the world, a strong case might be made for at least perpetuating the present level of $50 million annually spent on oceanographic research related to fisheries.

Potential economic benefits from marine biology are not restricted, moreover, to improved fish yields. The ocean appears to be a good

---

[5] Crutchfield, James, "The Marine Fisheries: A Problem in International Cooperation," American Economic Review, LIV, No. 3, 207–218 (May 1964).

source of other foods and pharmaceuticals. Marine biology might also be expected to contribute to improved techniques for depollution and sewage disposal (see secs. 3 and 6.4). Far more important, food from the sea can be used to improve world health, especially in underdeveloped countries. The foreign policy of the United States since the end of World War II has been committed to the view that U.S. prosperity and peace depend crucially upon improving living standards in the world at large, with particular emphasis on improving nutrition and health.

Specific estimates made by NASCO for improvements in near-shore sewage disposal and recreation are based upon extrapolation of present prices paid or imputed to recreational expenditures in seashore areas and upon cost reductions in sewage disposal. The estimates, at least on a gross basis, appear conservative. In particular, benefits from improvement in near-oceanographic environment are likely to extend well beyond recreational opportunities or cost reduction in sewage disposal. However, this depends on just how much people are willing to pay for improvements in their general living environment; for example, elimination of offensive odors or unsightly vistas. The ready and widespread Congressional acceptance of Great Society programs with similar orientations suggests that public valuation of these improvements is quite high. Probably the best argument for expanding the oceanographic effort in this area, in fact, is the potential complementarity with other Government programs for eliminating pollution, beach conservation and establishing seashore parks. An expanded oceanographic effort in relevant study areas (e.g., biology of estuarial regions and physics of wave action) would seem to be essential and proper support activity for these programs. Given this complementarity, the rather modest level of present expenditure at $10.5 million and the seemingly high benefits, some expansion of present programs relating to the near-ocean environment seems well justified (see secs. 3 and 4.8).

By contrast, considerable doubt surrounds any positive estimate of benefits to the United States from improvement of navigation and similar activities except for avoidance of rocks and shoals. There are good technical reasons for believing that the $364 million of benefits attributed to improved ocean navigation in the NASCO report are grossly overstated.[6] In short, the present level of nondefense ex-

---

[6] The NASCO report fails to consider interactions between different estimates. For example, direct savings in ship-construction costs, navigation costs, turnaround times, maintenance expenses and loading and unloading are all reported. It is reasonably clear, though, that the total required size of the ship fleet would be greatly affected by reported improvements in operating and maintenance procedures. Operating and maintenance costs would be reduced as the size of the fleet is reduced. Direct percentage reductions applied to present fleet and cost figures can therefore be misleading.

penditures on oceanography related to maritime improvements is probably of dubious value. At a minimum, any marked expansion would not seem wise, and very careful consideration should be given to some contraction. This program probably should be confined to activities aimed at port improvement, elimination of fouling and boring and any portion that might be related (in a byproduct sense) to defense. Research on containerization, hydrofoils and bubble ships suggested or sponsored by the Maritime Administration would seem to have more promise.

A potential bottleneck in the oceanographic program might be availability of research talent, although the expected increase in manpower in oceanography suggests this will not be a limitation (see sec. 9). Relationships between research and basic research expenditures in that program are therefore of interest; these are summarized in table 7.3 as they appear at present and in the recent past. Research might be defined, of course, in several ways: Broadly to include nonacademic as well as academic activities; with or without ship-operating costs included and inclusive or exclusive of different classes of engineering development. By the usual definitions, column (d) in table 7.3 seems to be the best estimate of basic research in the national oceanographic program, defined as expenditure for research in academic laboratories or in other laboratories organized in a similar manner. The figures are admittedly quite crude or approximate. (If one seeks estimates with ship-operating costs included, column (e) should be scaled up by about 50 percent.) It is interesting that the proportion of the total oceanographic program devoted to "basic research" in recent years is not too dissimilar (though slightly higher on average) to the *roughly* equivalent figures for other Government science programs, both before and after adjustment for ships or similar heavy hardware in other fields.

At present approximately $14 to $15 million (exclusive of ship-operating costs) is spent on basic research as part of the nondefense national oceanographic program. This implies that basic research is about 12 percent of the total expenditure of $120 million on nondefense missions. If this outlay of $14 to $15 million is expanded at a rate of 15 percent per year over the next 4 or 5 years, expenditures on basic research to support the nondefense national oceanographic programs would rise to a level of about $25 million (exclusive of ship-operating costs) by 1971. If the basic research component continues to be 12 percent of the total mission expenditure, this would imply an increase from $120 to $210 million per year in the total in a period of 5 years. Such an increase should provide sufficient scope for most justifiable programs now foreseeable in the nondefense sector. (The "sufficiency" will depend to some extent on the level of defense expenditures undertaken.) Presumably, most of the $25 million spent for basic research in 1971 on nondefense purposes would be channeled through NSF, Bureau of Commercial Fisheries or similar sources possibly connected with a new agency for marine and environmental programs. If biological aspects of the national oceanographic program are emphasized in the future, as advocated in this report, the proportion of academic research supported by the Bureau of Commercial Fisheries should be increased; this is in keeping with the NASCO recommendation that approximately $5 million for such purposes should be channeled through the Bureau in the future.

TABLE 7.3.—*Research in relation to total NOP expenditures (including defense)*

(a)	(b)	(c)	(d)	(e)	
		NOP Research expenditures as estimated by ICO [2]	Estimated expenditures on basic research [3]	Estimates of research as percent of total program	
Fiscal year	Estimated NOP total expenditures [1]			(c)/(b)	(d)/(b)
	Million dollars	*Million dollars*	*Million dollars*		
1963_____	155	31	NA	20	NA
1964_____	188	42	23. 9	22	13
1965_____	248	46	26. 1	19	11
1966_____	244	51	24. 6	21	10
1967_____	312	55	27. 5	18	9

[1] These figures are larger than those reported by ICO due to inclusion of some Naval oceanography not covered by ICO.
[2] After deducting an assumed one-third for ship-operating costs.
[3] Office of Science and Technology estimate of research conducted in academic institutions or equivalent private and Government laboratories, again exclusive of ship-operating costs.

The 15-percent annual growth figure in "basic" or academic research underlying these extrapolations is not magical, but it corresponds to recent growth rates or needs projected on reasonably conservative bases for such programs.[7] However, the very rapid increase in the expected number of oceanographers (see secs. 8.3, 9.4) suggests that the rate of increase of basic research may need to be substantially greater than 15 percent; therefore, basic research may represent a higher proportion of the $210 million budget.

A 5-year national oceanographic mission budget consistent with a $210 million total outlay is shown in table 7.4. Especially rapid growth is projected for environmental prediction and control and for near-oceanographic environment programs. On the basis of crude benefit assessments previously reported, these two would seem to be the most promising of today's nondefense oceanographic programs.

---

[7] "Chemistry: Opportunities and Needs," NAS–NRC, Committee for the Survey of Chemistry, 1965, p. 21; "Physics: Survey and Outlook," NAS–NRC, Physics Survey Committee, 1966, p. 118.

Substantial growth is also projected for marine biology and raw material surveys. An approximate 25-percent cutback in programs aimed at improvement of navigation, port improvement, ship routing, etc., is suggested, from a level of $38 million for fiscal year 1967 to a level of $30 million in 1971.

TABLE 7.4.—*Some suggested projections of nondefense national oceanographic budgets*

	Fiscal year				
	1967	1968	1969	1970	1971
Environmental prediction and control__	14. 5	25. 0	35. 0	45. 0	55. 0
Surveys relative to raw-materials development_____	12. 0	14. 0	17. 0	21. 0	25. 0
Marine biological resources_____	45. 0	48. 0	51. 0	55. 0	60. 0
Near-ocean environment_____	10. 5	15. 0	22. 0	30. 0	40. 0
Navigation aids, port improvements, etc_____	38. 0	36. 0	34. 0	32. 0	30. 0
Total_____	120. 0	138. 0	159. 0	183. 0	210. 0

The rationality of a sharp increase in the marine biological program budget depends to a considerable extent upon a political as much as an economic decision; namely, whether development of greater food yields from the ocean—a development which is likely to benefit primarily South American, Asian, and African countries—is a legitimate part of U.S. foreign policy. As noted, some good arguments can be made for such a view. Quasi-political judgments, of course, can be quite relevant in determining the level of other oceanographic programs as well.

Needless to say, programs perhaps not even envisioned today might be well justified in the future. New technological developments, moreover, could alter some basic assumptions built into these projections. Finally, it should be stressed that these extrapolations relate only to nondefense aspects of the oceanographic program; as indicated elsewhere in this report, the Navy program might properly experience a considerable expansion in the near future. In addition, the budget outlined in table 7.4 may not allow for sufficient development of expensive instrumentation or ocean engineering programs. This is not to say that there is no scope for such programs within these figures. Nevertheless, the possibility must be recognized that some relatively expensive, special projects may be needed in the nondefense budget; this will be particularly true if projects for deep sea submersibles and instrumentation improvements are not funded as part of the Navy's effort.

Strong arguments might be made for intermittently implementing even some of the more marginal instrumentation or engineering undertakings if: (1) It were deemed in the national interest to maintain more or less intact existing "systems engineering groups," in the aerospace, electronic, and similar defense industries; and (2) at some time these industries were to experience temporary, cyclic reductions in defense demand. Only temporary, as differentiated from long-term reductions in defense demands would justify such consideration. The economic argument would be that the cost of these system-engineering groups would be relatively low when employed on oceanographic undertakings during periods of temporary displacement from their normal activities. Needless to say, there are many complex issues involved in such a decision, not the least of which would be differentiating between temporary and long-term reductions in defense requirements and evaluating the cost of transferring system-engineering talents from one activity to another and back again.

An *ad hoc* character also surrounds decisions to invest in more ships for oceanography. As suggested elsewhere in this report, the major problem with regard to ship operations today appears to be funding of operating costs and allocating and combining use of ships for the needs of many small science projects. The budget projections presented in table 7.4 are consistent with the suggestions elsewhere in this report that the present need is not so much for more ship-operating funds as for better coordination and efficiency in use of ships (see sec. 10.6). The possibility should still be recognized that some upward adjustment in the table 7.4 figures could be required to properly fund ship operations. Certainly, very strong arguments exist for avoiding the situation of the recent past in which ships were seemingly kept operating only at the expense of cutbacks in basic research budgets.

A relatively modest budget in absolute terms seems to provide considerable scope for the orderly expansion of government-civilian activities in, on, and around the ocean. Such expansion, moreover, seems consistent with the development of basic oceanographic research, and academic support that is both feasible and not disproportionate to expected needs and development of other scientific fields. Finally, it is a budget that should meet major new needs for civilian ocean missions with a proper emphasis on expanded activities in particular sectors which appears to have the greatest potential for economic benefits.

8.0. Current Status

This section sumarizes the current status of marine science and technology in terms of recent history and predicted growth. We have attempted to minimize duplication with the reports of the National Academy of Sciences and the Interagency Committee on Oceanography,[1] and thus have not included a description of the number of laboratories and research ships. However, the current organization, financial support, and manpower are crucial to many of our recommendations.

8.1. ORGANIZATIONAL STRUCTURE

Activities in marine sciences and technology tend to be interdisciplinary and as a rule lack strong professional or academic traditions. Only recently have professional groups developed in ocean technology. Organizations concerned with broad aspects of geophysics and biology, as well as smaller groups devoted primarily to the oceans, are involved with scientific aspects of oceanography. As a result integration of work in marine science and technology is accomplished by complex interacting organizations and committees which differ in certain respects from those of other fields. Scientific and professional societies have committees, publications, and annual meetings. *Ad hoc* or continuing groups within industrial associations organize frequent symposia to consider special problems. News of general and particular industrial interest appears in trade publications. Directors of academic oceanographic laboratories meet, usually informally, to consider common interests. Regional associations coordinate activities of Government, industry, and academic groups. Organizations overlap to considerable extent; consequently, there is an intimate and fairly rapid exchange of information and opinion.

The Federal organization for marine sciences and technology de-

---

[1] "Oceanography 1960 to 1970," NAS–NRC Committee on Oceanography. Issued in 12 parts, 1959–60.

"Oceanography, the Ten Years Ahead," ICO Pamphlet 10, 1963.

"Oceanography, Achievements and Opportunities," NAS–NRC Committee on Oceanography (in preparation) ; we are indebted to the committee for allowing us access to current drafts of the manuscript.

serves special consideration because it is central to the national effort (see sec. 10 for a detailed discussion of the Federal organization). The Federal Council for Science and Technology, with membership comprised of a high scientific or professional official of each major operating agency and chaired by the President's Special Assistant for Science and Technology, is responsible for coordinating the agencies' activities in oceanography. The Council created an Interagency Committee on Oceanography, which has members representing more than 20 agencies with missions involving marine science and technology. The committee records and if possible coordinates the often overlapping programs of the agencies. The Interagency Committee since 1961 has prepared an annual report, the *National Oceanographic Program*, summarizing budgets, goals, problems, and achievements. The Interagency Committee has subpanels which make detailed studies on such subjects as "manpower" or "research ships."[2] With the aid of a small permanent staff the committee issues special reports in response to the many public inquiries about oceans. Through its many activities and those of its individual members, this committee provides the focus for national as well as Federal activities in marine science and technology.

International activities are also coordinated through a complex organizational structure. Coordination is accomplished through groups representing governments, such as the Intergovernmental Oceanographic Commission in UNESCO, and other groups which represent scientific societies within the International Council of Scientific Unions. The impact of these groups is manifest in such large projects as the International Geophysical Year and the International Indian Ocean Expedition.

8.2. SUPPORT

Federal support of oceanography has grown rapidly over the past 10 years. We have selected various measures to indicate this growth, ranging from the support of two older oceanographic laboratories (Scripps Institution of Oceanography and Woods Hole Oceanographic Institution) to the Federal budget for oceanography (fig. 8.1).

The most commonly used measure is the budget of the National Oceanographic Program, prepared annually by the Interagency Committee on Oceanography. It has grown from about $8 million in fiscal year 1953 to $220 million in fiscal year 1967. The pattern of growth appears to follow a logistic curve, with an exponential growth of 44 percent per year from some time before 1958 to 1963.

---

[2] "Scientific and Technical Personnel in Oceanography," ICO Pamphlet 21, November 1965.

"Undersea Vehicles for Oceanography," ICO Pamphlet 18, 1965.

The logistic curve was approaching a limit of $140 million by 1966, and growth ceased by loss of definition, a characteristic way for a logistic curve to stop. It is not surprising that oceanography which was easy to identify at the $8 million level should be less definite after a seventeenfold growth in funding. For fiscal year 1967 the program was redefined by ICO to include major components of oceanographic engineering in the MOHOLE and Deep Submergence Systems programs, among others (fig. 8.2). Consequent development may initiate a new period and type of growth.

The total Federal oceanographic budget includes defense components which are not included in the National Oceanographic Program. The total program, as reflected in the Federal oceanographic budget, continued its exponential growth until 1965, 2 years later than the National Oceanographic Program. It then fluctuated and now stands at about $310 million.

Components of marine science and technology supported by the Federal oceanographic budget are research and teaching in academic institutions. As the concept of oceanography has broadened, the proportion of the budget supporting academic research has decreased. A measure of academic oceanographic support is the sum of pertinent grants or contracts from the National Science Foundation and Office of Naval Research. This support grew exponentially from 1957 to 1963, then began to decline (fig. 8.1). Much of the growth in the period 1957–63 supported the establishment and strengthening of new oceanographic centers. As a result older laboratories received a smaller fraction of new money. The total Federal contribution to Scripps Institution of Oceanography and Woods Hole Oceanographic Institution grew exponentially from before 1955 and 1963, but at a slower rate than other components of the Federal oceanographic budget (fig. 8.2). During the next 2 years Federal support to these institutions was essentially constant, while the whole oceanographic budget continued to grow rapidly.

The pattern of Federal support which emerges seems reasonably clear. The whole budget and different components all grew exponentially from roughly 1958 to 1963. The doubling time was only 2 to 2½ years, however, and could not continue for many years without reaching an unsupportable level. Growth in different components of Federal support from 1958 to 1965 was as follows:

Fold

1. All support of SIO (Scripps Institution of Oceanography) plus WHOI (Woods Hole Oceanographic Institution) _____ 3
2. Selected support of all academic institutions_____ 6
3. National oceanographic programs_____ 9
4. Total Federal oceanographic program_____ 11

Beginning with nothing but basic research and education on a few campuses, marine sciences and technology have developed an under-

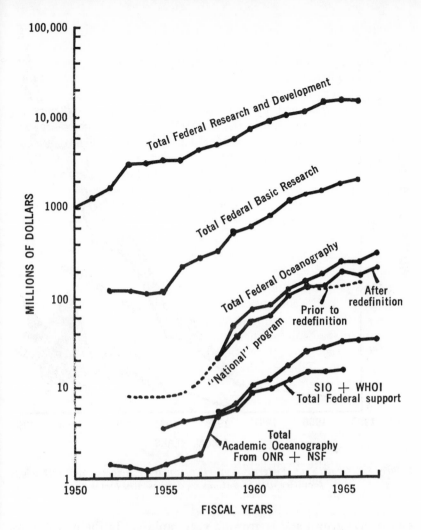

Figure 8.1. Growth of Federal support for different components of marine science and technology which are discussed in text

lying pyramid of research, development, and service for the Federal Government and technology and service for industry. Applied research and development have grown more rapidly than basic research, and it appears that technology in industrial components supported by the Federal Government is growing most rapidly of all.

Federal support of marine sciences and technology is supplemented by activities of State governments and industry. Funds attributable to State governments and industry were quite small only a few years ago, and we know of no summary of them. Consequently, we can only surmise from fragmentary information that support from these

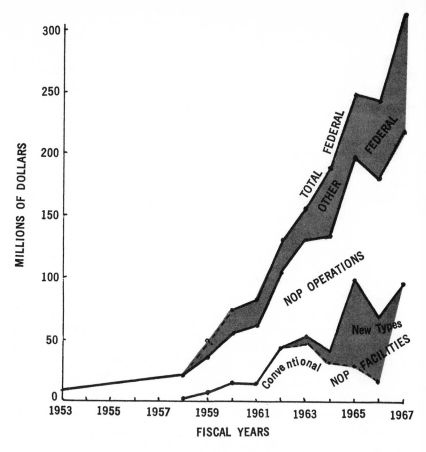

Figure 8.2. Growth of Federal support for marine science and technology facilities and operations as discussed in text

sources has grown and is growing very rapidly. In the past 5 years industry has produced a very substantial capacity in marine sciences and technology which is now backed by a fleet of ships (including deep submersibles), several field laboratories, large staffs and commitments for future growth. It is likely that this growth has been even faster than growth in Federal support in this field, but conclusive data are not available.

8.3. MANPOWER CONSIDERATIONS

Present Manpower. We estimate that about 500 to 600 professional oceanographers are active in the United States at present, even though comprehensive polls on the number, distribution, and training of oceanographers yield conflicting results. Further studies probably will not resolve differences because of the difficulty in defining an oceanographer. Accepting various definitions [3] in 1963–64 the total oceanographic science staff was 2,600 to 3,200, and the number of Ph. D.'s was 500 to 600. Other definitions yield different though similar numbers. Some 550 individuals, for example, are sufficiently well known to be listed in the latest International Directory of Oceanographers.[4] Another measure is the number of degreeholders in oceanography. A poll of the degree-granting institutions showed that 504 M.S. and 266 Ph. D. degrees have been granted to oceanographers over the past 20 years. An oceanographer in this definition is taken to be a degree-recipient with experience at sea and a broad knowledge of the ocean, regardless of the field of study. Finally, the number of oceanographers who produce scientific papers important enough to be cited by other scientists can be counted. Some 370 such individuals have been identified by our study, and a more comprehensive one might raise the number to 500. As in other sciences, however, 10 percent (37) of these cited oceanographers receive 50 percent of the citations. It should be noted that various attempts at measurement do not necessarily relate to the same people. Many oceanographers with Ph. D.'s did not receive them in oceanography.

Sources of Manpower. An oceanographer is a scientist or engineer whose work is concerned with the sea. Concern may have developed at any stage in his training or professional career. Manpower comes into the field in many ways, and opinions differ on what is ideal. Some of today's leading oceanographers took courses in oceanography, but many did not. The important point is that all scientists and engineers, regardless of training, are potential oceanographers. It may be difficult for a chemist to become a biologist, but it is relatively easy for him to become a marine chemist.

Students. We concern ourselves here only with graduate students working toward degrees in marine sciences. The number of students identified by the Interagency Committee on Oceanography and the National Science Foundation increased from 90 in 1960 to 290 in 1965 (fig. 8.3). These numbers, referring to students in "oceanographic departments" defined in a certain way, do not purport to be the total number in the marine sciences. Consequently, we polled 12 oceanographic departments and found that students working toward degrees at these places increased from 547 in 1963 to 763 in 1965 (fig. 8.3). This, once again, is not a complete list of students even in marine sciences, because oceanography is taught elsewhere. It does show that

[3] "Scientific and Technical Personnel in Oceanography," ICO Pamphlet 21, 1965. "A Study as to the Numbers and Characterisics of Oceanographic Personnel in the United States," Internat. Ocean. Fdn., Miami, Rept. to NSF, 1964.

[4] Vetter, R. C., An International Directory of Oceanographers, 4th ed., NAS–NRC staff rept., 1964.

there are more students than have been recognized and provides information on the rate of increase in their number.

Our data and ICO–NSF data show that the number of oceanography students has increased exponentially for the past 3 years. Moreover, students from these separate studies were proportional during 1964 and 1965. Using this relationship to extrapolate data back to 1960, the number of students at that time would be 220. On this basis, the number of students in 1954 would be 100; the number in 1947 would be 30. These figures seem reasonable in terms of the experience of Panel members. If these extrapolations can be accepted, the number of students increased exponentially for almost two decades at about the same rate that it has during the past few years.

The rate of increase for the past few years is 18 percent per year, and the doubling time is 4¼ years. If this trend, which probably has continued for a considerable length of time, prevails for only one more doubling period to fiscal year 1970, the number of students will exceed 1,500.

Degrees. The Interagency Committee on Oceanography and the National Science Foundation have determined the number of degrees granted in oceanography, defined with the same restrictions used in determining the number of students. They find the number of M.S. degrees is increasing sharply, but the number of Ph. D.'s is relatively constant (fig. 8.3). We have polled 12 degree-granting institutions. In 1962 and 1963, 17 and 16 Ph. D.'s, respectively, were granted, which is somewhat larger than the ICO–NSF determinations but indicates the same constant rate. In 1964 and 1965 a striking growth occurred to 28 and then 57 degrees, respectively. This growth is reflected in several individual institutions. The series for 1962 through 1965 at the University of Miami is 1, 3, 6, 10; at Scripps Institution of Oceanography it is 3, 2, 11, 17.

Growth in Ph. D.'s is exponential with a doubling time of about 1 year. That it may continue for another year is indicated by numerous spontaneous comments received in the course of the polling. For example at certain institutions more students received degrees at the middle of the present year than the whole of last year. At others which do not grant midterm degrees, many students have had theses accepted, although in the past theses have rarely been completed so early. Growth cannot continue for very long, because degrees are currently being granted to almost as many students as entered the institutions only 6 years ago. Presumably, the time required to earn a degree in oceanography has declined sharply in the last few years, as the number of students increases. Perhaps after 1 more year the rate of increase will drop to 18 percent, parallel to the increase in number of students. Even with such a dramatic drop, some 200 new Ph. D.'s will be granted in oceanography in 1970. Thus, the annual production of Ph. D.'s by 1970 will be of the same order as the total produced in the last two decades. We conclude that the rapid increase of Federal support to oceanography in the period 1958–63 has had a profound influence on the number of professionally trained oceanographers. This rapid increase, if accompanied by a continuation of the present budget, can only lead to major problems some 2 to 4 years hence.

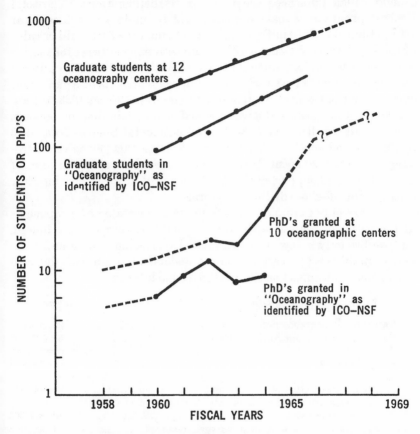

Figure 8.3. Growth of students and degrees in oceanography as discussed in text

8.4. NATIONAL INTEREST IN THE OCEANS

While we address ourselves in this report primarily to the Federal role in the oceans, we are fully aware that State and municipal governments and particularly private industry are important components of the national interest in the oceans. We believe that this awareness is evident throughout the report, in that we recommend strengthening Federal programs in the oceans which support socially and economically important activities by the States and private industry. We recommend, for example, increased support for near-shore oceanography, the subject of greatest immediate interest for recreation and pollution control. We recommend increased weather and sea-state predictions, which are urgently needed by the marine components of industry. However, it is useful to compare the Federal ocean program with other components of the entire national program to indicate the background which influenced the Panel in its deliberations. The total Federal program in marine science and technology for fiscal year 1967 is funded at $310 million. This is less than the $380 million value of the U.S. fisheries' catch in 1964.[6] Federal expenditures for marine science and technology during the past decade approach $1.5 billion.[6] During the same period U.S. petroleum companies spent a far larger sum on the Continental Shelves of this country. From 1953 to 1964, the Outer Continental Shelves yielded over $2 billion in bonuses, rentals, and royalties,[7] and the Inner Continental Shelves from 1956 to 1965 yielded another $963 million.[8] During this period the petroleum industry also spent $400 million on geophysical exploration of the shelves [9] and supported the development of a prosperous industry constructing off-shore drilling platforms.

These are only examples. A comprehensive catalog of components of the national interest in the oceans would be very lengthy indeed, and we list only a few statistics related to marine science and technology in table 8.1. We focus on the Federal program with due consideration of its impact on the whole national interest.

TABLE 8.1.—*Some statistics related to marine science and technology*

1. National oceanography program (1964) _____	$123, 000, 000
2. Navy classified oceanography (1964) _____	55, 000, 000
3. Army, Corps of Enginers (1964) _____	183, 000, 000
(a) Construction of harbors and channels (marine) ___	95, 000, 000
(b) Operation and maintenance, harbors and channels (marine) _____	84, 000, 000
(c) Beach erosion control, surveys, research_____	4, 000, 000
4. Maritime Administration (1964) _____	273, 000, 000
(a) Salary supplement_____	187, 000, 000
(b) Training_____	8, 000, 000
(c) Ship construction subsidies_____	78, 000, 000

[6] Department of Interior appropriation hearings, 1966.

[7] Carl Savit, hearings before Committee on Merchant Marine and Fisheries, H.R., Aug. 21, 22, 1963. Annual and accrued mineral production, U.S. Geological Survey, various years. Includes $771 million in dispute with Louisiana.

[8] Based on the Panel's correspondence with agencies of the States of Alaska, California, Louisiana, Oregon, and Texas.

[9] See Savit under (7) above.

5. Bureau of Commercial Fisheries, ship construction subsidies (1964) _____	$5, 000, 000
6. World fisheries catch (1964) _____ (billion pounds) ____	114
7. U.S. fisheries catch (1964) _____ (billion pounds) ____	5. 82
8. U.S. fisheries catch (1964) value 1964 _____	380, 000, 000
9. Value world fisheries 1964 _____	5, 000, 000, 000
10. Offshore geophysical exploration for oil (1961) _____	28, 000, 000
11. Total cost of U.S. offshore geophysical exploration for oil to 1965 _____	400, 000, 000
12. Bonuses, rentals, and shut-in gas payments, U.S. Outer Continental Shelf (1953–64) _____	1, 664, 000, 000
13. Royalties U.S. Outer Continental Shelf (1953–64) _____	388, 000, 000
14. Oil wells off Louisiana (1963) _____	4, 400
15. Expenditures of sport fishermen (1960) _____	2, 690, 000, 000
16. Value of outboard motors sold (1960) _____	167, 000, 000
17. Value of outboard motorboats sold (1960) _____	257, 000, 000
18. Bonuses, rentals, and shut-in payments, Inner Continental Shelf (1956–65) _____	411, 000, 000
19. Royalties Continental Shelf (1956–65) _____	552, 000, 000
20. Total revenues from U.S. Continental Shelf during about 10 years_____	3, 000, 000, 000

REFERENCES AND NOTES

1. ICO Pamphlet 17, January 1965.
2. ICO Pamphlet 17 gives DOD oceanography as $55 million—almost all Navy. DOD appropriation hearings, 1966, pt. 5 states only 47 percent of total Navy oceanography appears in ICO estimates for 1966. Classified, thus, is assumed equal to unclassified in 1964.
3. Presidential budget, 1966, 3 a, b, all identifiable expenditure on rivers eliminated.
3c. Federal expenses may not exceed one-third of cost.
4. Presidential budget, 1966.
5. Department of Interior appropriation hearings, 1966.
6. Department of Interior appropriation hearings, 1966.
7. Department of Interior appropriation hearings, 1966 ; equal to $100 million of GNP according to Economic Benefits from Oceanographic Research.
8. Pure guess at $0.05 per pound.
9d. Geophysics, v. 27, pp. 859–886. For 275 crew-months and estimated $0.1 million per month.
10. Carl Savit, hearings before Committee on Merchant Marine and Fisheries, H.R., Aug. 21, 22, 1963.
11. Annual and accrued mineral production, U.S. Geological Survey, various years. Includes $771 million in dispute with Louisiana.
12. See 10.
13. See 10.
15. Statistical abstract, 1964, ocean component not identified.
16. See 15.
17. See 15.
18–20. Based on Panel's correspondence with agencies of the States of Alaska, California, Louisiana, Oregon, and Texas.

9.0 Education and Manpower

9.1. GENERAL REQUIREMENTS IN OCEANOGRAPHIC MANPOWER

It is very difficult to anticipate absolute future needs for oceanographic manpower. In the future oceanographers may be employed by liberal arts colleges and universities, oceanographic departments and institutions, Gvernment agencies and industry. They may serve on foreign assignment as experts or may train administrative support personnel including those for ships. Numbers that will be needed are most uncertain. For example we do not know whether or not liberal arts colleges and universities will be giving courses in oceanography in the next 20 years. The Panel believes, however, that projected figures for manpower discussed in section 8.3 are sufficient to meet foreseeable needs. Of greatest concern to the Panel is not the number being trained, but the quality of their education.

9.2. EDUCATION FOR RESEARCH WORKERS

As noted before it is possible to begin work related to oceans at any level of academic training or even after formal training has ceased. At the time an individual receives a Ph. D., he is qualified to do research (and teaching) in at least a limited field. This limited field may be exhausted rapidly, however, or may expand in unexpected directions. If the scientist is narrowly trained and unable to start over again, his career as a researcher may be concluded a few years after it begins. In contrast if his training is broad, he has little difficulty in following wherever his work leads or in transferring his interest to some new and exciting sector of research. Although the number of Ph. D.'s in oceanography is increasing very rapidly, the proportion that are adequately trained in basic physics, mathematics, chemistry or biology is small. Thus, the large number should not give us comfort, because only a much smaller group is equipped to be effective in applying new techniques from contemporary science to problems in the ocean. Some individuals with oceanographic training have made contributions to a wide range of scientific fields, but these are exceptions.

Most educational institutions have discontinued undergraduate training in oceanography, reasoning that at least an undergraduate degree in fundamental sciences is necessary for effective work in the highly competitive oceanography of the future. A Ph. D. in oceanography may be too specilized if it exerts a negative influence on the intellectual level of oceanography. This is reflected in research programs, in vaguely defined objectives that purportedly justify world-encircling expeditions and even in lack of focus on proposed national programs in oceanography. The limitations of depth in graduate training in oceanography have caused concern in some academic oceanographic centers. Consequently, a broad background in basic sciences is required for admission to some graduate schools. It is also increasingly common for advanced training in basic science and mathematics to form an integral component of graduate education in oceanography. This is a very promising development which may eventually produce a larger percentage of Ph. D.'s in oceanography capable of full, productive careers in research and training. Another hopeful development is the establishment of educational programs in the broad area of environmental sciences. The close linkage of oceanography with other environmental sciences and with basic sciences has been illustrated throughout this report and supports the thesis that classical Ph. D. training in oceanography will not serve the purposes of ocean science and technology in the years ahead.

If oceanographers receive most of their education in basic science, mathematics, and environmental sciences, it may be possible to educate them in places other than oceanographic laboratories. If a biology department in any university has a few or even one professor interested in the oceans, he can direct thesis research and produce students capable of undertaking careers as oceanographers. The actual research may require some use of special facilities in an oceanographic or marine biology laboratory. However, it may be even more dependent on a reactor or an advanced computer which may be available at the university but not at the marine laboratory. The need for special facilities provides one reason for organizing associations of universities and oceanographic laboratories. Arrangements can be made for joint degrees, exchange of lecturers or some other appropriate relationship. In this way the number of students trained in basic science with marine-oriented theses could be substaintially increased at a relatively low cost. Rather than establishing new oceanographic laboratories, numerous existing ones could be expanded to accommodate visiting graduate students and professors. The Panel believes that restricting education to a few oceanographic institutions will exert a debilitating effect on long-term development of oceanography. We would prefer to see a wide variety of institutions throughout the country have a few faculty members interested in oceanography and capable of directing student theses even though some portion of the work will be taken at a special facility which has limited, if any, relationship with the university.

Some system is needed to attract scientists whose interest in the oceans is aroused only after they have received Ph. D.'s. It seems certain that the most effective but difficult way to recruit oceanographers would be to effect a postdoctoral transistion; for example, from a Ph. D. physics education to research in oceanography. A favorable environment for such transition would exist if university and oceanographic laboratory associations which we have suggested are formed. If faculty members in university departments of basic sciences do research on marine aspects of their disciplines, students may be expected to consider similar research careers. It should be emphasized that these remarks apply to research and teaching in engineering as well as science. In fact the recent history of engineering education may be cited as a precedent for the whole discussion. Engineering students take increasing amounts of mathematics and basic science, and training for various specialities is almost indistinguishable. Oceanographic engineering research thus generally will be performed by very broadly trained engineers.

In the future many university departments may include faculty members whose research is ocean-oriented, provided that the research standards in the field compare favorably with those in other areas. Spreading oceanography into more universities is thus critically dependent on raising research standards related to the oceans to the quality maintained in other sciences.

9.3. EDUCATION FOR TECHNOLOGY AND COMMERCE

Some areas of the industrial community have suggested that aerospace engineers should do oceanographic engineering if defense or space requirements should slacken. This substantiates the point that a career in marine technology or commerce may be based on education which is not marine-oriented. On the other hand, the oceanographic environment is complex and little known, and it would be surprising if oceanographers now being trained at oceanographic laboratories did not remain in demand for marine technology and commerce. Marine mining, aquiculture, geophysical survey, pollution control, and the like will require individals with broad understanding of the complete marine environment.

9.4. IMPLICATIONS OF MANPOWER CHANGE

The rapid increase in students and degrees which we have identified (see sec. 8) has had a marked effect on Federal support for oceanographic education. The total number of NSF and ONR contracts and grants to oceanography gives a measure of Federal support. By this measure the support granted for Ph. D.'s has declined by 67 per cent during the past 2 years. If both support and degree output grow at expected rates, present support per individual will decrease nearly 90 per cent by 1970. This does not mean that it will be small compared to other sciences. At present, Federal support is $170,000 per year per Ph. D. granted, a figure which is substantially higher than Federal support of about $39,000 per Ph. D. in chemistry but of the same order of magnitude as that for high energy physics. If all qualified students who wish graduate education in oceanography are to receive training in the present style, support will be grossly inadequate by 1970. However, an unrestricted expansion of the present style of education is not a desirable goal. The alternative of education through associations between universities and oceanographic laboratories should be less expensive as well as more fruitful than expansion of laboratories alone. On the other hand, it is evident that some expansion of laboratories, especially student facilities (including housing), will be essential regardless of the mode of oceanographic education.

9.5. MARINE STUDY CENTERS

In a few universities graduate departments other than environmental sciences have become increasingly involved in ocean-oriented research and education. Adoption of the recommendations of this report would accelerate this trend by calling attention to the highly interdisciplinary nature of many of the most important and interesting problems involved in ocean science and technology. The report naturally emphasizes scientific and technological challenges. However, we are critically aware of numerous legal, social, and economic problems posed by the proposed redirection and expansion of our efforts in the ocean.

Work in interdisciplinary areas would be facilitated by the establishment of Marine Study Centers, whose role would be not only to foster studies on applications of science and technology to the sea, but also to relate them to underlying natural sciences and to social sciences—economics, sociology, psychology, politics, and law—as they are affected by and in turn affect occupation and exploitation of the sea.

We visualize Marine Study Centers as centers of advanced study, not as degree-granting departments. We *recommend* a Federal grant program for developing this capability in institutions already deeply involved in marine-science study.

10.0. Federal Organization and Program

10.1. FEDERAL INTEREST—PAST AND PRESENT

Federal involvement in marine science, oldest of the Federal Government's scientific pursuits, began with the Coast Survey's founding in 1807 to meet the needs of the Nation's navigators. Over the years other agencies manifested need for knowledge of the sea, but federally sponsored marine-science programs did not gain momentum until 1956. At that time a group of Government oceanographers, stimulated by advances realized under Navy sponsorship dating from World War II and impressed by opportunities the imminent International Geophysical Year presented, initiated activities which produced today's greatly expanded program.[1]

A major report on the national importance of knowledge of the seas with a recommended program for its pursuit was produced in 1959, under a Government contract, by the National Academy of Sciences Committee on Oceanography. This report, a prototype of many which have subsequently appeared, motivated increased Federal interest and support for oceanography and also raised serious questions in industry and Government about the adequacy of the programs planned for exploring and understanding the seas.

The intensity of present interest within the industrial community and in Congress is well illustrated by the lengthy congressional hearings held in the summer of 1965 regarding some 19 bills submitted during the first session of the 89th Congress. These and subsequent bills reflect a widespread impression that the Nation's marine interests are not being adequately pursued by the executive branch. This is commonly attributed to organizational fragmentation of Federal responsibility for oceanography and to lack of a sufficiently high-level advocate for ocean science and technology.

The executive branch's position has been that oceanography has advanced rapidly in the last 5 years under the leadership of the Federal Council for Science and Technology with the coordination pro-

---

[1] An excellent historical summary is given in the preface of "National Oceanographic Program," ICO Pamphlet 24, 1966, which is included as app. IV of this report.

vided by its Interagency Committee on Oceanography. The Marine Resources and Engineering Development Act of 1966 incorporates the first two approaches. The Act establishes a National Council on Marine Resources and Engineering Development, chaired by the Vice President and with Cabinet level members. The Council has very broad responsibilities to advise and assist the President in furthering the effective use of the sea. The Act also establishes a Presidential Commission on Marine Science, Engineering, and Resources consisting of 15 members drawn from "Federal and State governments, industry, universities, laboratories, and other institutions engaged in marine scientific or technological pursuits." The Commission is charged with making a comprehensive investigation of all aspects of marine science and submitting a report not later than eighteen months after it is established. The Act provides that the Council will exist for 120 days after the submission of the Commission's report. (See app. VI for the entire Act.)

Three general approaches to the problem have appeared in the Congress:

1. Establish a presidential commission of distinguished scientists and laymen outside the Government to study the problem and advise the President concerning what should be done.

2. Establish a council composed of appropriate cabinet members, headed by the Vice President, to develop and coordinate a comprehensive "national" program.

3. Establish a new agency composed of those agencies now engaged in oceanographic research and development, excluding perhaps those within the Navy. This new organization has been referred to as a "wet NASA."

10.2. FEDERAL ROLE IN A NATIONAL OCEAN PROGRAM

The Panel does not feel that it is the Federal Government's responsibility to plan or carry out the entire national ocean program. State governments, municipalities, private industry, and individuals motivated by local interests, profit, zest for adventure or curiosity should and must be counted on to devise and execute much of the desired program. There are, however, four Federal functions necessary to assure that the results are in balance and compatible with the national interest:

1. Enunciate national policies with regard to furthering U.S. marine interests.

2. Foster exploration, development and use of oceans and their resources through the establishment of appropriate financial, le-

gal, regulatory, enforcement, and advisory institutions and measures.

3. Describe, predict, and develop capabilities for modifying the environment.

4. Initiate, support, and encourage programs of education, training, and research and provide technical services and facilities for relevant activities in science and technology.

Today, about 20 Federal agencies are concerned with ocean affairs. Each plays some role in one or more of the above functions, and all four are carried out to some degree at the Federal level.

It is obvious from a review of present agencies' activities, however, that only the last two functions are to any degree well developed and coordinated across agency lines. The first two functions, articulating national ocean policy and fostering exploration and use of the seas, are greatly in need of systematic development and implementation by a more centralized authority; and all four would benefit from it.

10.3. PRESENT ORGANIZATIONAL STRUCTURE

Support of oceanography as broadly defined in the United States is shared by a large number of agencies. Table 10.1 lists the contributions of various agencies to the National Oceanographic Program as defined by the Interagency Committee on Oceanography. As has been discussed in section 7, the National Oceanographic Program does not include all oceanographic activities of the Federal Government; table 10.1 does, however, reflect the relative contribution of various agencies

TABLE 10.1—*National Oceanographic Program budget, fiscal year 1965–67*

[In millions]

Agency	Actual, fiscal year 1965	Estimated, fiscal year 1966	President's budget, fiscal year 1967
Defense	98.0	80.5	113.5
Commerce	20.1	13.1	16.4
Interior	20.2	19.5	19.4
National Science Foundation	44.0	43.2	43.0
Atomic Energy Commission	6.0	11.6	13.5
Health, Education, and Welfare	5.2	6.3	[1] 9.7
Treasury	2.0	2.1	2.3
Smithsonian Institution	.9	1.5	1.6
State	.4	.5	.5
Total	196.8	178.3	219.9

[1] Includes $3.8 million for the Federal Water Pollution Control Administration which was transferred to the Department of the Interior on May 10, 1966.

to the total program. The large jump between fiscal year 1966 and fiscal year 1967 reflects the rapid growth of a new Navy project—the Deep Submergence Systems Project.

Table 10.2 presents the ICO breakdown of the National Oceanographic budget according to various functions. These numbers should be taken as a qualitative distribution. For example, our evaluation suggests that in fiscal year 1967 basic research in oceanography, exclusive of ship-operating costs, will total $27.5 million or about 9 percent of the total Federal program in oceanography (see sec. 7.2).

Following is a brief summary of agencies involved in the oceanographic program, with a short description of mission, level of interest, and relevance to the national program. This listing is meant only to provide an overview of the agencies' activities. Far more detailed information is available in the annual ICO reports on the national program.[1]

TABLE 10.2.—*ICO breakdown of the National Oceanographic budget fiscal year 1965–67*

[In millions]

	Actual, fiscal year 1965	Estimated fiscal year, 1966	President's budget fiscal year, 1967
Research [1]	70. 5	81. 4	84. 3
Surveys	26. 3	29. 5	38. 4
Ocean engineering	62. 0	40. 7	66. 0
Ship construction	20. 7	12. 5	16. 2
Instrumentation	10. 3	9. 4	8. 4
Facilities	6. 0	3. 5	5. 2
Data center	1. 0	1. 2	1. 4
Total	196. 8	178. 2	219. 9

[1] Includes International Indian Ocean Expedition and Ocean Sediment Coring Program.

Department of Defense

Navy activities in oceanography are divided between those directed toward solving specific Navy problems and those involving a broad support of oceanography through Office of Naval Research contracts with universities, nonprofit institutions, and industrial laboratories. The Navy not only is a major supporter of basic research, but is also the principal contributor to survey programs through the U.S. Naval Oceanographic Office and to the development of ocean engineering, primarily through the Deep Submergence Systems Project. This

[1] The latest, "National Oceanographic Program, fiscal year 1967," ICO Pamphlet 24, 1966.

project is funded at $32.8 million for fiscal year 1967. The Navy thus plays a dominant role in the country's oceanographic programs, with very heavy emphasis on the development of undersea technology. The Panel has recommended continuation of Navy responsibility in this area (see secs. 4 and 5).

ARPA maintains a small program (about $100,000) of seismicity study in the ocean and hydroacoustic seismic wave propagation, in support of their program for detecting underground nuclear explosions.

The *U.S. Army Corps of Engineers* supports oceanographic research with the intent of improving navigation, flood control, and shore restoration and protection. The work is conducted at CERC (Coastal Engineering Research Center) and at a few universities and private institutions. Total budget of the Corps of Engineers attributed to oceanography by ICO is $2.3 million.

Department of the Interior

In 1962 Congress authorized the *U.S. Geological Survey* to extend investigations into the ocean. The principal emphasis in the program has been continental-shelf explorations and a very limited mapping program has begun. In the past year, the Geological Survey has participated extensively in the JOIDES program and has in fact been the major Federal operational participant in this program, althought the main financial support comes through NSF. For fiscal year 1967 the agency listed $0.9 million.

The *Bureau of Mines* is authorized to determine the industrial value of marine minerals and to develop techniques for sampling and recovery. In recent years the Bureau's activities and interests in ocean resource development have increased, with a proposed fiscal year 1967 budget of about $200,000, mostly for development of recovery systems, although the Bureau has investigations of "representative" problem areas underway.

The *Bureau of Commercial Fisheries* has, under Federal directive, broad responsibilities to conduct investigations on the abundance and biological requirements of fish and it also has statutory responsibility for management of marine food resources. The bulk of oceanographic activities of BCF, about $14.3 million, is classified as research by ICO. BCF also conducts limited survey operations and has underway a program to develop fisheries technology.

The *Bureau of Sport Fisheries and Wildlife* limits its activities to research on game fish within 20 miles of shore. According to ICO, anglers in this area catch about 11 billion pounds of fish annually, but other estimates are much lower (see sec. 2.3). At present ICO states that BSFW spends $600,000 in research, largely concerned with life histories and studies of game fish relative to their distribution in space and time.

In May 1966, the *Federal Water Pollution Control Administration* was transferred to the Department of Interior. This agency was established originally within the Department of Health, Education, and Welfare under the Water Quality Act of 1965. The oceanographic activities of FWPCA are concerned with water supply and pollution control. Of a total budget of $3.8 million in fiscal year 1967, $2 million is designated for research.

Department of Commerce

The *Environmental Science Services Administration,* which includes the former Coast and Geodetic Survey and Weather Bureau, in fiscal year 1967 requested $11 million to conduct survey operations, mostly near our shores. Some money is being spent to improve the technology of these surveys. A research program of $2.3 million includes support of the sea-air interaction laboratory.

The *Maritime Administration* sponsors a $50,000 program to study ocean-wave spectra and their effects on ship motions. The purpose of the Maritime Administration's program is to understand better the nature of the ocean surface and its effect on operation and design of merchant ships.

Department of the Treasury

Coast Guard oceanographic observations are conducted at four stations manned by the Coast Guard—two in the North Atlantic and two in the North Pacific. In addition, Coast Guard ice patrol ships carry out oceanographic investigations. The Coast Guard oceanographic budget is about $2.3 million for fiscal year 1967, $65,000 of that amount to be used for research.

Department of Health, Education, and Welfare

The oceanographic work of the *Public Health Service* supports the basic PHS mission, safeguarding the public's health. Of the total of $5.6 million in fiscal year 1967 $1.1 million is connected with research on shellfish and $2.3 million is for the *National Institutes of Health* which supports research programs in marine biology that have biomedical importance.

In fiscal year 1967 the *Office of Education* will provide about $300,-000 worth of fellowships in oceanography.

Department of State

The Department of State supports work conducted by eight international fisheries commissions. Two of these, the Tuna and Halibut

Commissions, support oceanographic fisheries programs. In fiscal year 1967 the State Department budgeted about $0.5 million.

Atomic Energy Commission

Oceanographic work of the AEC is primarily concerned with problems of dispersal of radioactive elements in oceans. This includes investigations of biological uptake of radioactive elements, sedimentation and chemical interaction, and ocean circulation and mixing. In fiscal year 1967 the AEC budgeted $4.6 million for research from a total of $13.5 million.

National Science Foundation

By means of grants and contracts of $43 million in fiscal year 1967, NSF supports basic investigations in biological and physical oceanography at universities and research institutions. Fiscal year 1967 programs involve $6.7 million for biological oceanography, $8.0 million for physical oceanography and $2.3 million for Arctic and Antarctic programs. The ocean-sediments coring program is listed for $1.3 million and MOHOLE for $19.7 million.

Smithsonian Institution

The *Smithsonian Institution* carries out investigations on marine populations and distribution of organisms with emphasis on systematics, and on sediments in the ocean. The total program for fiscal year 1967 is $1.6 million.

National Aeronautics and Space Administration

NASA has no program in oceanography listed in the reports of ICO. NASA has sponsored conferences on uses of satellites in oceanography and may be expected in the future to have substantial oceanographic interests. The agency obligated $900,000 in fiscal year 1966 for a feasibility study of oceanography from space with the Navy acting as agent.

Role of the Interagency Committee on Oceanography

The Interagency Committee on Oceanography of the Federal Council for Science and Technology has been charged with the task of developing each year a "national oceanographic program." It was to do this by reviewing current activities and planned programs of individual agencies, engaging in coordinative budget planning and considering special problems that arise in implementing the national program, recommending solutions thereto. In fact one of the initial aims and goals of ICO was to introduce into a federally sponsored program more facilities, ships and manpower to provide a broad base on which to build scientific and technical aspects of national programs. As has been discussed earlier in the report (see sec. 8), ICO was remarkably successful in meeting these objectives.

Examining the relationships between agencies and ICO, the Panel came to the conclusion that ICO can serve effectively in the role of transmitting information among various agencies and providing help on questions of policy coordination and detailed technical planning, involving the several agencies. For example ICO has been fairly successful in coordinating and disseminating information on ship schedules, but it has been unable to carry out detailed technical planning for major programs such as the proposed stepwise buoy program (see app. II).

Furthermore, ICO has been unable to develop new missions transcending the limited missions of individual, participating agencies. As a result there is no National Oceanographic Program in the sense of the whole being greater than the sum of individual parts defined by existing agency missions. A minor exception is the Sea-Air Interaction Laboratory, which is yet to develop. In the Panel's view the biggest deficiency has been the failure to define a national goal for development of biological resources beyond the rather narrow concept of commercial and sport fisheries (see sec. 2). The Panel does not believe the ICO could undertake the Federal function of setting national policy.

Role of External Advisory Groups

The present program in oceanography has been heavily influenced by reports of the Committee on Oceanography of the National Academy of Sciences-National Research Council. The Academy's Committee on Oceanography resulted from the feeling of an informal committee of marine scientists within the Government that oceanography needed support. The Academy's committee has since served as a leading advocate for oceanography. However, it should be recognized that an outside group cannot really change national policy when it involves more than the current missions of agencies.

10.4. ORGANIZATION FOR THE FUTURE

If one examines present agency activities against the four governmental functions defined in section 10.2 quite clearly the Government is doing very well in meeting its responsibilities in supporting programs of research and education. NSF and ONR have developed strong support for academic activities in oceanography, although these need to be broadened beyond oceanographic institutions (see secs. 4.11, 5.4, 9). On the whole the Panel believes that both NSF and ONR have discharged their duties well. Beyond the provision of ships, laboratories, and the National Oceanographic Data Center, the Federal Government has done little to provide technical services and facilities. We see an increased need for such facilities, and we expect the Navy to play a much more important role in the future than it has in the past.

Some progress in describing the environment has been made, but our abilities to predict are still minimal (see sec. 6). Responsibilities for description and prediction are scattered throughout the agencies. The Navy supports a large survey program, as does ESSA, while smaller survey programs are found within Bureau of Commercial Fisheries, Geological Survey, and Coast Guard. The Navy, Coast Guard, and ESSA are all involved in the prediction problem, but the techniques remain primitive and do not reflect substantial advances in theoretical oceanography.

Fostering development of biological resources of the ocean is the responsibility of BCF, while the Bureau of Mines, and Geological Survey have statutory responsibilities regarding mineral resources.

No single agency has prime responsibility for developing and advocating national policy, although each agency on occasion develops programs of oceanography which further the particular agency's mission.

We could recommend continuation of the present organizational framework with words of caution regarding the importance of coordinated efforts. We do not believe this to be the wise course. For example one of our major recommendations is to develop the technology for improved use of marine food resources. Such activity naturally falls into the domain of BCF. A cursory examination of the required program, however, reveals that it would depend very heavily on physical oceanography. For example, thorough studies of upwelling and turbulent fluxes are required for proper implementation of certain phases of the program. Prediction of the environment is important. Would this mean that BCF should develop its own capabilities in physical oceanography, turn to ESSA or engage the Navy?

ESSA is primarily charged with development of prediction techniques for furtherance of commerce. Its rightful emphasis is on prediction of storms and research undertaken within the agency has little to do with problems of improving marine food technology. BCF could seek help from universities or industrial concerns, but again this would duplicate efforts of other environmental agencies. This brief example illustrates some of the problems the Panel foresees in implementation of its major recommendations within the present administrative structure.

The Panel *recommends* a major reorganization of non-Navy governmental activities in oceanography. The recommended reorganization would place in a single agency all those Federal activities related to *description, prediction,* and *attempts* to develop capabilities of modifying the environment (ocean, atmosphere, and solid earth) and those activities concerned with managing and developing resources of the ocean. The proposed reorganization emphasizes the unity of environmental science and observational technology.[2] This unity is one of the themes of this report and has been discussed at length in sections 2, 3, 4, 6, and 9. For example, progress in description and prediction of the ocean environment can be made only with recognition that the ocean and atmosphere form a *coupled system*, each affecting the other in important ways.

The second basic motivation for reorganization is the fact that the ability to work within the oceans, to develop the oceans' resources and to use the oceans depends very heavily on our proficiency in describing and predicting the environment. Exploration of mineral resources on the Continental Shelf requires the ability to work not only along the sea bottom, but in the water column above as well. Prediction of sea-bottom conditions and conditions in the water column will be as important in the next 20 years as the prediction of weather and wave heights at the surface.

In summary the reasons for the proposed reorganization are:

1. Unity of environmental sciences and observational technology.

2. Dependence of oceanic development for industry and commerce on our ability to predict the environment.

3. Clearly establishing responsibilities for executing national objectives and nondefense missions for the oceans.

In broad outline the reorganization would combine activities of the Environmental Science Services Administration, the Geological Survey (both its land and ocean activities), oceanographic activities of the Bureaus of Commercial Fisheries and Mines, and a portion of the Coast Guard's oceanographic activities. Such grouping would provide an agency competent to deal with the four functions of government listed in section 1. The Panel does not make any recommendations as to whether the new agency should be independent or part of an existing agency.

With the creation of a new agency oceanographic activities of the Nation would be supported in five ways:

1. By the NSF in its traditional role in support of fundamental studies through grants and fellowships with special emphasis on aspects that contribute to manpower education for ocean science and technology.

---

[2] See app. V for a note on the testimony of J. W. Powell who recognized the same unity and recommended roughly the same reorganization to Congress in 1884.

2. By the new agency in carrying out its responsibility for management of the environment and ocean resources and for providing description and prediction services through a balanced program of direct participation and support of industry and universities.

3. By the Navy in carrying out its mission of national security through its laboratories and industry and through ONR support of civilian institutions, as well as by its supporting role in the development of undersea technology and provision of national test facilities.

4. By agencies such as AEC and HEW in carrying out their missions.

5. By the Smithsonian Institution in fulfilling its unique obligation to systematic biology.

In summary the proposed new agency would be an operating agency whose mission is to provide for effective use of the sea by man for all purposes to which we now put the terrestrial environment. The agency's responsibilities would be broader than just the quest of new knowledge and understanding. In addition, in the provision of prediction and description services the agency would be responsible for the atmospheric and solid-earth environment.

The creation of a mission-oriented agency with major responsibilities for ocean development of science and technology does not by itself provide a clear mechanism for coordination, planning, and budgeting. Several agencies, the Navy and NSF in particular, will continue to have major responsibilities in ocean-oriented activities. The need for information interchange and dissemination now discharged by ICO will continue and we *recommend* formation of an interagency group under the Federal Council for Science and Technology to provide services now rendered by ICO and the Interagency Committee on Atmospheric Sciences. This group should also have responsibilities for information interchange involving the solid-earth sciences. This group would thus link the activities within the new agency with those in other agencies for all the environmental sciences.

Budget allocations between the new agency, NSF, and the Navy would be on a competitive basis, recognizing the mission responsibilities of the new agency and the Navy. The Federal Council, the Bureau of the Budget, and Congress would all participate in the budgeting process. Though the proposed agency does not solve all problems of budgeting, it does provide a centralized authority with major mission responsibility for the oceans.

The proposed reorganization will create a multitude of political and social problems. However, at present a unique opportunity exists to develop an organization capable of assuming major responsibility for the national goal of the effective use of the sea by man. Achieving this capability will be worth the problems.

10.5. LEGAL PROBLEMS

In several sections of this report Panel recommendations envisage action in the oceans which might involve political and legal problems arising either from the present structure of the international law of the sea or from demands for changes in that law. The frequency and gravity of possible legal problems are now difficult to project, since much depends upon the type, scope, and timing of ocean operations which may be undertaken in the future by this and other countries and upon attitudes and practices of other nations. However, there is realism in present concern about these possibilities, because the existing international legal structure was largely developed under conditions that differ greatly from those likely to prevail in the foreseeable future. The task of adapting this legal structure to rapidly changing conditions can quite conceivably generate stress in relations between nations in the form of lively, perhaps dangerous controversy. The strategic significance of the ocean environment and the urgent need for acquiring greater knowledge of it, emphasized throughout this report, combine to warrant apprehension lest developments in international law adversely affect the national interest. It is partially for these reasons that the Panel *recommends* Federal support of Marine Study Centers.

Relevancy of law to the national ocean program may be illustrated by discussing one of the Panel's major *recommendations*, as well as certain of the more specific subsidiary recommendations, from the standpoint of legal considerations involved.

(1) The need for greater knowledge about and understanding of the oceans.

Although the Panel *recommends* pursuing scientific investigation for describing and understanding marine phenomena, processes and resources (see sec. 1.1) as a separate goal of the national ocean program, it is apparent that increased knowledge and greater understanding are fundamental to achievement of all our objectives in use of the oceans. Therefore, significant interference with scientific research from the existing or future legal regime of the sea could pose serious obstacles to the entire national ocean program. That there is occasion for concern about this matter is plain. As this report amply demonstrates, for purposes of scientific inquiry, observation, and detailed investigation throughout the area and volume of the vast oceans are required, including the benthic boundary. But for purposes of political authority the oceans are now fragmented into parts, sometimes only vaguely defined, some of which are not accessible for scientific research. Thus, the territorial sea and internal waters of various nations with limits varying from nation to nation and measured by variously determined base lines, are wholly removed from investigation of any kind without prior consent of the nation within whose territory the waters are located. In somewhat similar fashion certain inquiries of a purely scientific nature (such as geologic surveys, benthic boundary studies and certain biological investigations recommended by the Panel) cannot be undertaken on the Continental Shelf without obtaining consent from adjacent nations. It should be emphasized in this connection that the seaward limit of the Continental Shelf is but vaguely defined, according to the presently applicable law, and possibly may be expandable to embrace extremely large regions of the ocean floor. Moreover, if in the future nations are permitted to acquire exclusive use of fishery resources in greatly enlarged ocean areas, such as claiming all fishery resources in waters above the Continental Shelf or by some other comparably extensive method, the task of obtaining biological and ecological knowledge of important seafood resources could be frustrated entirely or at least severely handicapped. Neither these resources, nor their proper study can be compartmentalized within artificially determined ocean boundaries if the information necessary for devising wise programs of control and management for international benefit is to be acquired.

Since effective implementation of the national ocean program requires increased understanding of the sea, there is definite need both for continued study of effects on scientific research of extending various types of national boundaries into the oceans and for assuring that this vital aspect of the national interest receives appropriate protection.

(2) Control and management of marine food resources (see sec. 2).

The Panel noted that for foreign policy reasons development and improvement of technological capabilities of the United States for marine food exploitation deserve high priority in the national ocean program and that other countries have already taken the lead in this aspect of ocean exploitation. The increasing need in many parts of the world for sources of protein coupled with the presence of significant amounts of protein food in the oceans appears likely to increase international competition and to emphasize the importance of control and management of these resources. The present system of legal regulation of these international resources, under which fishery resources of the high seas are open to exploitation to everyone without restriction, is widely regarded as inadequate in light of anticipated demands. Among the major problems to be expected in attempting to create efficient and equitable schemes for control and management are continued efforts at expansion of territorial sovereignty into the oceans, either by enlarging the territorial sea or perhaps by attempting to acquire domination over rich fishery areas that are not contiguous to any nation and to secure vast extensions of coastal national control specifically for the purpose of gaining exclusive access to fisheries in zones contiguous to the demanding nation. If, as seems desirable, international agreement is to be the principal mode for regulating these resources and for providing the necessary control and management, major problems may be expected in reaching an international consensus about appropriate limits on exploitation, methods for limiting exploitation and allocation or sharing of permissible yields. It is possible that entirely new international institutions and procedures must be created if optimum use of these international resources is to be realized. The Panel believes that intensive multidisciplinary study is needed of relevant factors which are likely to be encountered in the course of these developments.

(3) Employment of bottom-mounted installations and equipment (see secs. 4, 5).

Implementation of the national ocean program envisaged by the Panel requires use of the ocean bottom for positioning instrumentation and equipment for a variety of purposes, including emplacement of laboratories and test stations. Potential international legal problems involved in these operations appear to depend on precise locations employed, various characteristics of the equipment or installation and the specific assertion of national authority demanded over the area concerned. If equipment or installations (manned or unmanned) are to be emplaced within the ocean territory of other nations, including in this context the Continental Shelf, problems of the type already discussed under (1) above may be expected, as well as others.

The precise scope of the adjacent nation's authority over activities by other nations on its Continental Shelf, which is described in the Continental Shelf Convention as "sovereignty" for certain purposes, is not yet fully delineated, but it extends at least to certain kinds of scientific research. In addition it is conceivable that these ocean-floor activities, whether undertaken on a foreign Continental Shelf or on that contiguous to the United States, entail interference or conflict with other kinds of activities in the same area, depending on characteristics of the equipment or installation on the bottom and the nature of the area's other uses. Even for otherwise permissible undersea operations there might be a need, therefore, for specific efforts at accommodation with other activities. It should be noted again, for emphasis in this context, that the region of "Continental Shelf" within the authority of the adjacent nation has not yet been determined finally, and the possibility exists that under the current vague definition of the continental shelf enormous expanses of the ocean bottom may come to be regarded as subject to certain controls by a particular nation.

Difficult questions are also involved if emplacement of equipment or a manned installation, such as a laboratory or test station, in high-sea regions beyond the Continental Shelf of any nation entails also the claim to some degree of exclusive use of the area, perhaps amounting to temporary or permanent acquisition of the area as part of national territory. In connection with Man in the Sea operations the interest of national security may make it necessary or strategically desirable to occupy areas of the ocean for extended periods (see sec. 4). Contemporary conceptions of the international law of the sea evolved before it was technologically feasible to occupy areas of the ocean floor for extended periods, hence it appears that the legal consequences of such uses of the ocean floor require consideration of applicable principles of law and desirable adaptation of these principles to anticipated conditions.

(4) Buoys.

The Panel *recommends* a well-planned system of employment of buoys as an important method of implementing the national ocean program (see sec. 6, app. II). Numerous legal problems may be encountered as the system is developed and expanded, including issues about (*a*) access to various parts of the oceans subject to differing legal regimes; (*b*) principles to be employed in determining liability for damage, deliberate and inadvertent, to the buoys and to vessels; (*c*) prescriptions for theft protection of the buoy system and the data it contains; and (*d*) principles for allocating jurisdiction to adjudicate disputes involving the above issues.

(5) Development of new materials in the ocean (see secs. 4, 7, app. III).

The present need for substantial government investment in development of raw materials in the oceans is questionable, because reliance can be placed upon market forces and upon private experience in appraising the economic attractiveness of these ventures. Nevertheless, there appears to be an obvious governmental role in providing a legal framework within which development can take place if and when it appears desirable. To the extent that absence of the protection afforded by such a framework deters initiative by indsutry in developing the hard-mineral resources of the ocean, for example, only government initiative can provide a remedy. Even if economic considerations are not now favorable for expansion of hard-mineral exploitation to deep-sea areas, the possibility of improvement in circumstances due to technological breakthrough, emergence of different market conditions and changes in political relations warrant study and continued appraisal of the situation in anticipation of eventual government action to provide a satisfactory legal basis for effective exploration and exploitation.

10.6 SUPPORT AND OPERATION OF OCEANOGRAPHIC SHIPS

Current American oceanographic ships are for the most part operated by oceanographic laboratories through grant and contract funds from the Federal Government. This mode of operation developed during the 1930's when Woods Hole, Scripps, and some biological laboratories each operated a single ship in coastal and nearby oceanic waters. This method of operation made good sense, because almost all oceanographers were at these few laboratories; ships were inexpensive to operate; and scientists and crews were partially interchangeable, especially on sailing ships. This mode of operation has continued even though oceanography has changed rapidly. At present ships cost at least 10 times what they did in the 1930's. Crews and scientists have far more specialized abilities and are rarely interchangeable. An increasing number of oceanographers are not members of major oceanographic laboratories and have corresponding difficulties in obtaining time on ships. Finally, the MOHOLE platform, drilling ships and the Antarctic research ship, *Eltanin*, among others, are operated as national facilities because they are too expensive for individual laboratories. We believe that the funding, scheduling and operations of most oceanographic ships should be revised in order to make them more economical and effective and to broaden opportunities for all American scientists and engineers to use federally owned and supported ships, reducing the burden on oceanographic laboratories of maintaining large marine facilities.

In the past the system of ship operations was flexible and responsive to scientific objectives. This may be attributed to the fact that ships were scheduled by scientists and were under the operational control of scientists. These virtues must be preserved and some radical action may be necessary at this time to do so. Ships are already being scheduled more than 2 years in advance; this is hardly flexibility. Large ships are used to test lightweight gear near ports because laboratories have only one ship, and it is large; this is hardly responsiveness.

Reasons for changes in ship funding are almost self-evident. At present the operating cost of a ship is met by a conglomeration of grants and contracts. The daily cost is commonly determined retroactively by dividing the annual cost by the number of operating days. Thus, an unpopular, small ship may cost more per day than a popular, big one. This mode of funding came to a crisis in fiscal year 1966 when many new ships had been built, and insufficient funds to operate them had been requested by the supporting agencies. The problem has not yet been solved. This mode of operation may be contrasted with the method used by the Navy to keep books on ships provided for its own laboratories. Before a ship is built, the Navy makes an operation commitment for its expected life. Operating expenses are then funded separately from the cost of, for example, oceanography for which the ship is used. The same comprehensive budgeting system should be used for oceanographic ships. Funding need not be through a single agency at this time. The Navy should agree to support some ships by block-funding. Others could be funded as they are now by the National Science Foundation, and we *recommend* support by a line item in the budget of the new environmental agency which is recommended in this section.

Central block-funding will permit effective planning on use of oceanographic ships. It will not, however, solve the problem of equitable distribution of ship time to all qualified scientists regardless of affiliations nor eliminate the problem of ship operations at small oceanographic laboratories. These problems should be dealt with by formation of ship-user groups with joint responsibilities and privileges. Such user groups already exist on an informal basis, because the larger oceanographic laboratories tend to regard themselves as national facilities. Occasionally these laboratories have assigned ship time to scientists from other institutions simply because they had good projects and had no other way to get a ship. Some laboratories have even shown willingness to form user groups with neighboring universities and assign equal priority to all applications for ship time from group members. Thus, there is every indication that laboratories are willing to share ship time, yet numerous scientists from nonoceanographic institutions cannot go to sea. This seems to reflect inadequate communication and indicates the need for a more formal organization of potential ship users.

The problems of small laboratories with excess ship capacity of some types and not enough capacity of others can also be solved by forming user groups. A small laboratory has difficulty in using a single, usually large, ship effectively. On the other hand, several laboratories and a group of associated universities would form an efficient user group. The group could perhaps consolidate ship-support operations at one large shore facility, thereby reducing costs. The group would also have several ships of different sizes and capabilities and could assign the most effective one for a particular project.

Therefore, we *recommend* that in general oceanographic ships be grouped into reasonable sized, regional fleets; perhaps three or four (fleets) would serve the Nation's needs. The fleets should be assigned to independent, regional organizations representing user groups of oceanographic laboratories and universities. The organizations should be comparable to the user groups which exist in high energy physics. Every effort should be made to include in the user group those institutions which at present do not have formal activity in ocean science and technology.

96

Assignment of operating responsibility for a regional fleet to an oceanographic institution will increase an already heavy bureaucracy at these institutions. It is important that this administrative apparatus not be allowed to overwhelm the research and educational efforts of the institution. Concern with the bureaucracy has prompted this suggestion to establish indepedent user groups.

Fleets could be based in one place or dispersed, depending on available operating facilities. User groups may be built around single, large oceanographic laboratories or a cluster of small ones. Rigid guidelines or formulas for formation of user groups should not be established if they can be avoided. However, formal organizations will be necessary to increase flexibility and, perhaps, economy in oceanographic operations and to give all qualified scientists equal access to ships supported by the Federal Government.

The essential characteristic of ship operations must be responsiveness to scientific aims. The ship must be under the complete control of the chief scientist in all matters that do not affect its safety or internal workings of the crew. This requires a great deal of understanding among scientists, crew, officers, and senior scientists in particular. We propose that this understanding be achieved by education. All officers of oceanographic ships should have training in oceanography in order to understand the scientists' objectives. This might be done by correspondence courses in part, but a 1-year program leading to an M.S. in oceanography would be far preferable. The Coast Guard and Navy, for example, already have farsighted programs of graduate training in oceanography for their officers. The training could be accomplished when officers are rotated to shore. On the other hand, no one should be designated chief scientist on a ship who is not familiar with officers' problems concerning privileges of the crew, safety at sea required by law, and similar matters. A seminar course for scientists with participation by officers might provide an ideal solution, although training for junior scientists could be given at sea during expeditions.

10.7. NATIONAL FACILITIES

In sections 4 and 6 certain national facilities such as test ranges required for proper advance of ocean science and technology have been considered. In this section we propose additional facilities for marine studies.

National Oceanographic Data Center

The National Oceanographic Data Center was established to acquire, process, store, and disseminate oceanographic data for scientific, commercial, and military purposes from virtually all sources in the United States and from many foreign sources. NODC pursues its objectives through four branches: preparation, processing, quality control, and information.   The Center is funded through contributions of various agencies.

Despite determined efforts of the NODC staff, quite clearly the Center falls far short in meeting demands of users.   Furthermore, a study is needed to determine means for improving exisitng services and for broadening and extending the scope and versatility of services in response to a wide spectrum of user requests.

The Center's importance will increase as both federally and privately sponsored activities in the ocean increase.   Services of NODC need upgrading very badly, and this will require a substantial increase in funding, which is at present $1.4 million.   The Panel *recommends* that the National Oceanographic Data Center be placed within the new agency recommended previously.   Furthermore, to properly carry out its function as the country's chief supplier of oceanographic data, the Center should develop capability for research in problems of data analysis and information retrieval.   All this implies a substantial increase in funding.

Laboratories and Facilities for Specialized Marine Studies

Experimental and long-term studies on marine communities and organisms and on man's ability to remain beneath the surface of the sea will require new types of specialized facilities.   Once created, these facilities will make possible unique experimental approaches in these major research areas.   They will be high in cost and special in nature. They should be administered so as to permit their use by investigators from many institutions, thus assuring full use over long periods of time.   They should be appropriately located, whenever possible, near universities or other scientific centers for the contributions that such centers can make.

Advances in both science and technology in several major areas of oceanography are presently hampered by lack of suitable facilities. In section 6 certain facilities required for development of physical oceanography (buoy systems, deep-sea instrumentation) were discussed.   In section 4 a facility of value to a wide range of technological efforts was considered.   This section is concerned with facilities of importance to two areas of marine biology :

1. Direct observational, experimental study of deep sea organisms.

2. Basic applied studies required to permit man to remain beneath the sea surface for long periods of time.

Five categories of facilities of specialized types are required and *recommended* for work in these two areas :

1. One or more medium-sized surface vessels suitably equipped for capture, maintenance, observation, and experimental study of deep sea organisms.   Medium-sized vessels will be suitable for

most studies if careful choices of working areas are made. Calm surface conditions over most of the year are present over deep waters close to shore on the lee sides of many oceanic islands (the Channel Islands off southern California, Hawaiian Island, Tongue of the Ocean in the Bahamas, Galapagos). Sizeable populations of deep sea organisms occur in these waters.

2. Several undersea vehicles of varying depth and range capabilities, suitably equiped for the observation, capture, transport and experimental treatment of deep sea organisms.

3. One major shore facility for maintenance, observation and experimental study of deep sea organisms. This facility should be located as convenient to deep water as possible. It might serve as a base of operations for a ship of the type listed above. Equipment in this facility should be compatible with that used on shipboard, to allow transfer of organisms without temperature, pressure, or light shocks. Shore equipment should include aquaria instrumented to produce controlled temperatures, pressures, and light intensities.

4. One major shore facility fully equipped for the range of basic studies required by Man in the Sea (see sec. 4.11). This facility should be associated with a university medical research center.

5. Several fully instrumented, movable submersible laboratories for basic studies of man living beneath the sea surface for extended periods of time. Full logistic and manpower support for these laboratories should be provided. The Navy's program in this direction should continue to be encouraged, with adequate opportunities for nonmilitary, basic studies carried out by other organizations.

In marine biology as in physical oceanography, the Panel does not foresee the need for any additional large, multiocean survey vessels. This view reflects the belief, documented throughout this report, that oceanographic research is progressing into a new era in which emphasis should shift from broad surveys to oriented efforts.

Development of biological resources of the sea requires study of the Arctic, Antarctic, tropical, and temperate waters. Each of these environments supports characteristic biological communities and organisms living under special conditions. In order to study these communities and their component organisms experimentally and to learn their potential usefulness, special laboratories are required to serve as centers for their subject regions and to permit simulation of certain major, environmental conditions of these regions. The United States presently has no suitably equipped laboratories of these types. Serious attention should be given to the establishment of the following laboratories.

1. ***Arctic Marine Laboratory*** with controlled environmental facilities for the maintenance and study of communities and organisms of Arctic waters, including studies of subfreezing temperatures. Its location should be adjacent to northern waters to permit direct support of field studies of Arctic marine environments as well as laboratory investigations.

2. ***Tropical Marine Laboratory*** with controlled environmental facilities for maintenance and study of communities and organisms of tropical regions. Its location should be tropical to permit support of field studies of tropical marine environments as well as laboratory investigations.

3. ***Temperate Zone Marine Laboratory*** with controlled environmental facilities for maintenance and study of communities and organisms of the temperate seas, especially those of the open oceans, including food fishes. Its location should be readily accessible to the open sea to permit direct support of field studies as well as laboratory investigations.

Supply of Marine Organisms. Important advances in biology and medicine often result from discovery of an experimental organism ideally suited for exploration of the biological system being studied. In fact, so often do we see a correlation between breakthrough and experimental organism that we suspect the ready availability of exploitable biological systems may provide the key to rapid expansion in many biological disciplines (see sec. 6.4).

No center currently exists from which living marine organisms can be obtained in good supply, although there are already centers where stocks of certain biological materials can be acquired. A national center for distribution of marine animals should be established. Such a center, however, should be developed around certain prerequisites. It must, for example, be located near major air transport facilities. The center should also enable culture and supply of animals in a synthetic medium which can be controlled and which is reproducible. The center should have a good collecting staff, and it should be physically able to obtain, hold, and supply organisms which are seasonal in occurrence and which do not occur in the immediate area. The center may eventually but will probably never reach a self-supporting status; therefore, continuing Federal support will probably be required.

The National Fishery Center and Aquarium appears to be the agency which could best perform this service, and we *recommend* that funding be provided to operate and construct such a facility. The center would serve as an information clearinghouse concerning availability of marine organisms which it would not routinely attempt to supply.

This important function, when added to the already recognized education-research function, could serve to make the National Fishery Center and Aquarium an indispensable and important part of the Nation's research in marine and other fields of biology.

11.0. Priorities

The Panel has not attempted to offer a detailed blueprint of the national program for the oceans but believes it is essential to recognize a long-term goal which has been identified as the effective use of the sea (sec. 1.1). The Panel has examined opportunities in technology, science, education, and management vital to attaining this goal.

11.1. OCEAN SCIENCE AND TECHNOLOGY

The Panel assigns highest priority to those efforts in oceanography that deal with national security. The problems outlined in section 5 clearly indicate need for developing the capability of operating anywhere in the oceans, either by manned or unmanned vehicles, at any time. We are a long way from achieving this capability. The Navy should continue to be the lead agency for that part which pertains to national security.

The Navy in its Deep Submergence Systems Project is making an intensive effort at achieving part of this capability. We give this program a high priority, and we feel it should be expanded, including extramural consultation and participation. The requirements for achieving the capability include:

1. Development of large working volumes at atmospheric pressure.

2. Development of tools, manipulators, and semi-remote-control power tools and support structures.

3. Development of small underwater systems having powerplants in the 10- to 100-kw. range, which will require a greater emphasis on fuel-cell power systems than the Navy has so far supported.

4. Knowledge about the long-term effects of high pressures on man (see sec. 4.11).

In terms of national security we feel high priority should be given to studies of the benthic boundary, since weapon systems of the future may be deployed on the ocean floor, and to basic studies of weather in the oceans at all scales. These studies are needed for construction

102

and operation of undersea structures and are critical to the **ASW** problem.

We *recommend* that the Navy continue and expand its support of basic research through ONR. It has made highly successful contributions through research and education in the past, and we expect it to continue to do so in the future.

In the civilian sector the Panel gives highest priority to two related problem areas: Development of food resources and development of capability for environmental prediction.

The economic analysis in section 7 suggests that greatest economic returns can be expected from progress in environmental prediction and control. For the oceans the field is still in the research stage, although sound conditions can be predicted to a limited degree in connection with ASW problems. The buoy programs discussed in section 4.9 and appendix II are given high priority by the Panel. This is based on scientific interest and on environmental-prediction need as emphasized in sections 6.1, 6.2, and 6.3. Buoys and related instrument development will provide essential data regarding weather in the oceans and the nature of the ocean-atmosphere interaction.

While development of food resources does not rate high on an economic basis, viewed strictly in domestic terms, it can contribute in a very major way to the Nation's international position (see secs. 2, 7.2, and 10.5).

The Panel assigns a very high priority to development of coastal regions for recreation and commerce; these functions will be possible only if the quality of the near-ocean environment is maintained and improved. The problems here are unusually complex, since they involve badly understood science, engineering with a high failure rate and a variety of legal and social problems. The Panel believes that standards of coastal engineering can be raised only by active participation of university groups. There is need to enhance research at CERC as well as at other laboratories.

The Panel gives low priority to continuing hydrographic surveys in their present form. Methods employed are outmoded, slow and are not responsive to user requirements. We believe that *high priority* should be assigned to development of survey technology as discussed in section 4.6.

In the area of management the Panel believes the present administration of the Federal program is unacceptable, and major revisions are required if the country is to progress toward the goal of effective use of the sea. The Panel has outlined in section 10.4 one possible reorganization scheme. This scheme appears logical to the Panel in view of the close interdependence of environmental sciences, resource development, use of the ocean and environmental description, and prediction. Because the proposed reorganization may create severe political problems, the Panel wishes its major recommendations to stand apart from those regarding reorganization. However, the Panel assigns a very high priority to questions about present administration of the Nation's ocean program.

In the field of education the Panel assigns highest priority to developing means by which scientists from a wide variety of fields and institutions can be brought into research in the oceans. It is important to develop cooperative arrangements between universities throughout the country with oceanographic facilities.

In particular the Panel views its recommendations with regard to ship provision (see sec. 10.6) as a major step in furthering the goal of effective use of the sea. The heavy overburden of bureaucracy associated with ship management deadens the intellectual life of laboratories and should be lessened. Our solution is to provide block-funding for the ships and organize the ships into regional operating fleets under "user group" management.

11.2. OCEAN SCIENCE AND TECHNOLOGY IN COMPARISON WITH OTHER FIELDS

It is difficult in dealing with such complex subjects as oceanography to list priorities within the subject. Even more difficult is the task of comparing oceanography with other fields of science and technology, although this kind of comparison is essential in developing a total national plan.

Oceanography in the nondefense agencies is characterized by the fact that the percentage of total budget devoted to research and development is high; the percentage devoted to basic research is similarly high. In terms of total expenditures for the national oceanographic program, basic research makes up about 10 percent; whereas in other fields of science and technology the percentage devoted to basic research is 10 percent of research and development, rather than of the total program.

We cannot compare oceanography, for example, with the high energy physics program, since that program is devoted entirely to science and is thus 100 percent basic research. Perhaps a large governmental program most nearly paralleling oceanography is the space program, which is something like 90–95 percent research and development and, like oceanography, has a similarily high percentage of basic research.

We believe the present oceanographic program can be justified to a large extent on the basis of its contributions to national security and to civilian economy. We feel that a much stronger program can be developed along the lines outlined in our report and that oceanography should receive a higher priority in the national planning than it has in the past. For example in any competition for funds with the space program the case for oceanography would be very good. In making this statement we recognize many intangibles which are often used to justify programs.

It is far more difficult to compare expenditures in oceanography with expenditures in Great Society programs whose science and technology component is relatively smaller. We suggest that meaningful although incomplete comparisons can be made using the analysis outlined in section 7. In any event oceanography as conceived in this report complements or supplements many facets of Great Society programs.

Panel Membership and Activities

In the course of formulating this report, the Panel on Oceanography and its Subpanel on Marine Biology gathered information in a number of ways. Among these were visits to laboratories, interviews with representatives of Federal agencies and industry and interviews with knowledgeable individuals. In addition representatives of the agencies listed in this appendix met with the Panel and Subpanel during some of their meetings. Twelve oceanographic institutions were polled for data summarized in the report. In all, the Panel and Subpanel spent 29 days (18 for Panel and 11 for Subpanel) in formal meetings starting in July 1965 and ending in April 1966. The Panel, Subpanel on Marine Biology, places visited, people contacted, and Federal agencies interviewed are given below.

In addition to contacts through meetings, each of the Panel members, Subpanel members, and staff having 20 different private, academic, and governmental affiliations, during their professional activities made contacts with a large number of individuals. During the existence of the Panel several hundred professional oceanographers and marine biologists with industrial, governmental, and university affiliations were contacted in this manner. No attempt has been made to tabulate these informal contacts, but they should be recognized as an important part of this study.

Captain Edward Snyder met with the Panel on numerous occasions. He provided detailed information on many aspects of the Federal program as a representative of Dr. Robert Morse, chairman of the Interagency Committee on Oceanography.

The Panel encountered many problems involving legal questions, which it discussed with Mr. Michael Cardozo and on his recommendation sought the advice of another distinguished expert, William T. Burke, of Ohio State University. Professor Burke reviewed the entire draft report and raised numerous substantive questions regarding law. A portion of his comments form the basis for section 10.3 and many other suggestions have been taken into account in the preparation of the final draft.

In addition to the industrial representatives on the Panel and those members of industry contacted formally before the Panel and informally by the Panel members, appendix III includes a report formally submitted to the chairman of ICO and to the Panel.

PANEL ON OCEANOGRAPHY

DR. GORDON J. F. MACDONALD, *Chairman*
Institute of Geophysics and Planetary Physics
University of California, at Los Angeles

Dr. DOUGLAS L. BROOKS
President
The Travelers Research Center, Inc.

Dr. ROBERT CHARPIE
Union Carbide Corporation

DR. ROBERT FLEAGLE
Department of Atmospheric Sciences
University of Washington

DR. FINN J. LARSEN
Director of Engineering
Honeywell Incorporated (until November 1965. Now Deputy Director Defense Research & Engineering)

DR. WILLIAM D. MCELROY
Chairman, Department of Biology
The Johns Hopkins University

Dr. JOHN MEYER
Department of Economics
Harvard University

DR. WALTER H. MUNK
Institute of Geophysics and Planetary Physics
University of California, La Jolla

DR. JACK P. RUINA
Institute for Defense Analyses

DR. HENRY STOMMEL
Woods Hole Oceanographic Institution

DR. GERALD B. WHITHAM
Chairman, Department of Applied Mathematics
California Institute of Technology

Technical Assistants

DR. HENRY W. MENARD
Office of Science and Technology
Executive Office of the President

CMDR. JOHN C. FRY
Office of Science and Technology
Executive Office of the President
(Temporary Duty—June/October 1965)

SUBPANEL ON MARINE BIOLOGY

Dr. WILLIAM D. McELROY, *Chairman*
Chairman, Department of Biology
The Johns Hopkins University

Dr. EDWARD W. FAGER
Scripps Institution of Oceanography
University of California, La Jolla

Dr. MALCOLM S. GORDON
Department of Zoology
University of California, Los Angeles

Dr. FRANCIS T. HAXO
Scripps Institution of Oceanography
University of California, La Jolla

Dr. C. L. MARKERT
Chairman, Department of Biology
Yale University

Dr. ROSS F. NIGRELLI
Director, Osborn Laboratories of Marine Sciences, N.Y. Aquarium
New York Zoological Society

Dr. CARL H. OPPENHEIMER
Director, Oceanographic Institute
The Florida State University

Dr. LUIGI PROVASOLI
Haskins Laboratories

Dr. JOHN H. RYTHER
Woods Hole Oceanographic Institution

Dr. KARL M. WILBUR
Department of Zoology
Duke University

Dr. WARREN J. WISBY
Director, National Fisheries Center and Aquarium
Department of the Interior

Technical Assistants

Dr. HENRY W. MENARD
Office of Science and Technology
Executive Office of the President

Dr. CLAIRE L. SCHELSKE
Office of Science and Technology
Executive Office of the President

LABORATORIES VISITED BY PANEL ON OCEANOGRAPHY

Applied Physics Laboratory
University of Washington

Biological Laboratory
Bureau of Commercial Fisheries
Seattle, Wash.

Department of Oceanography
University of Washington

Hawaii Institute of Geophysics
University of Hawaii

Institute of Marine Science
University of Miami

Navy Electronics Laboratory
San Diego, Calif.

Scripps Institution of Oceanography
University of California, La Jolla

Sea Lab II Operations Center
La Jolla, Calif.

Woods Hole Oceanographic Institution
Woods Hole, Mass.

The Director and Associate Director of Lamont Geological Observatory, Columbia University, were consulted on laboratory activities at the panel meeting in New York City.

LABORATORIES VISITED BY SUBPANEL ON MARINE BIOLOGY

Biological Laboratory
Bureau of Commercial Fisheries
La Jolla, Calif.

Institute of Marine Sciences
University of Miami

Scripps Institution of Oceanography
University of California, La Jolla

Tropical Atlantic Biological
Laboratory
Bureau of Commercial Fisheries
Miami, Fla.

AGENCIES INTERVIEWED BY PANEL

Atomic Energy Commission

Bureau of Commercial Fisheries

Bureau of Mines

Department of Commerce

Department of Health, Education,
and Welfare

Department of the Interior

Department of the Navy

Department of State

Environmental Science Services
Administration

Interagency Committee on
Oceanography

National Oceanographic Data Center

National Science Foundation

Smithsonian Institution

U.S. Coast Guard

U.S. Geological Survey

AGENCIES PARTICIPATING IN SUBPANEL ON MARINE BIOLOGY

Atomic Energy Commission
Division of Biology and Medicine

Bureau of Commercial Fisheries
Division of Biological Research

Department of Health, Education,
and Welfare
Division of Environmental Engineering and Food Protection
Shellfish Sanitation Branch

Department of the Navy
Oceanic Biology Program

Federal Water Pollution Control
Administration

National Institutes of Health

National Science Foundation
Division of Biological and Medical
Sciences

Smithsonian Institution

INDIVIDUALS IN SPECIAL CAPACITIES CONSULTED BY PANEL ON OCEANOGRAPHY

R. ABEL
Interagency Committee on Oceanography

M. CARDOZO
Association of American Law Schools

W. M. CHAPMAN
Van Camp Foundation

J. H. CLOTWORTHY
Westinghouse Electric Corporation

W. K. DAVIS
Bethtel Corporation

A. LANE and T. P. MELOY
National Security Industrial Association

J. A. KNAUSS
University of Rhode Island

R. MORSE
Chairman, Interagency Committee on Oceanography

M. B. SCHAEFER
Chairman, National Academy of Sciences Committee on Oceanography

A. SPILHAUS
University of Minnesota

L. G. WEEKS
Consultant on World Oil

CONSULTED BY PANEL MEMBERS, BUT NOT BY FULL PANEL

W. BASCOM
Ocean Science and Engineering

T. COLEMAN and R. BETTS
Ocean Systems, Inc.

J. DUNNING
Mayor's Advisory Council on Science and Technology (New York)

J. M. GILLEAN
San Diego Chamber of Commerce

C. KIRKBRIDE and others
Industrial Panel (See app. III)

J. KYGER, J. CLARK and others
Oceanography Subcommittee, National Association of Manufacturers

P. PETERSON and others
Bell and Howell

T. PRYOR and others
Oceanic Institute and Sea-Life Park

J. WENZEL
Lockheed

110

LABORATORIES AND OTHER PLACES VISITED BY INDIVIDUAL PANEL MEMBERS AND STAFF

Bureau of Commercial Fisheries

Bureau of Commercial Fisheries
Biological Laboratory
Honolulu, Hawaii

Chesapeake Bay Institute
Johns Hopkins University

Cloud Physics Laboratory
University of Hawaii

Department of Oceanography
Oregon State University

Environmental Science Services
Center
Washington Science Center

Fleet Numerical Weather Control
Monterey, Calif.

Interagency Committee on Oceanography

Marine Biological Laboratory
Woods Hole, Mass.

Narragansett Marine Laboratory
University of Rhode Island

National Oceanographic Data Center

Naval Oceanographic Office

Naval Postgraduate School
Monterey, Calif.

Smithsonian Institution

Smithsonian Institution
Scientific Information Exchange

Stanford University

OCEANOGRAPHIC CENTERS POLLED FOR DATA

Alan Hancock Foundation
University of Southern California

Chesapeake Bay Institute
Johns Hopkins University

Department of Geology and Geophysics
Massachusetts Institute of Technology

Department of Oceanography
Oregon State University

Department of Oceanography
Texas A. & M. University

Hawaii Institute of Geophysics
University of Hawaii

Institute of Marine Science
University of Miami

Lamont Geological Observatory
Columbia University

Narragansett Marine Laboratory
University of Rhode Island

Oceanographic Institute
Florida State University

Scripps Institution of Oceanography
University of California, La Jolla

Woods Hole Oceanographic Institution
Woods Hole, Mass.

Moored Buoy Array Program

1. THE SIGNALS TO BE READ ARE COMPLEX

There is in the velocity, temperature, and salinity fields of the ocean a richness of unexplored phenomena. What the "water bottle" oceanographer regards as noise, or what he often dismisses as "internal waves," "variability," or "turbulence" is in fact a host of fluid dynamical processes. Far from being noise, these evidences of variability are actually signals which, could we read them, would tell us much about the internal dynamics of the ocean which we do not presently know.

Present-day buoy technology provides means for exploring these new dimensions of oceanic phenomena. The actual use of moored instruments has been limited to efforts of individuals who, lacking resources, logistic support, and necessary organization, have to date been unable to maintain a dense enough array of instruments for long enough time to gather statistically significant data. Signals are complex, and a sophisticated measuring program will be required to read them. This problem would be difficult enough if all fluctuations in deep oceans were due to a broad spectrum of linearly superposed internal gravity waves of random phase plus some tidal lines. Even in such a hypothetical case many sensors would be necessary to separate vertical modes, and many horizontally spaced points would be necessary to discriminate wavelengths and to determine dispersion relations and directional properties. But all fluctuations in the oceans are not due to internal gravity waves; there are stirring motions, local instabilities generating turbulence and presumably exotic convective structures due to the unstable salinity distribution. There will also be long-period eddies and Rossby waves, for example.

2. DETECTION AND VERIFICATION OF INTERNAL GRAVITY WAVES AS AN EXAMPLE OF SIGNALS TO READ; FOUR-MINUTE SQUARE

Among the many processes taking place simultaneosuly in oceans is the radiation of energy within the body of ocean water by means of internal gravity waves. It has a well-developed linear theory.

Isolated sets of short-duration observations have been made (O. V. Schubert, Ufford, Cox, Fofonoff). Some show evidence of internal tides, directional propagation, several vertical modes and inertial motions. Preliminary discussions of any of these results immediately lead to questions which can be resolved only by significantly more complicated deploying of buoys and sensors. As an example one can cite measurements of water temperature at Bermuda (1958: Haurwitz, Stommel, and Munk) in which long-duration measurements were obtained at the cost of mounting only two thermistors on the sloping bottom. More thermistors at various depths in the open oceans would have clearly been better but were beyond the technical resources and money available. It is clear that multiplication of sensors is the direction in which we must go; this means that oceanography must deliberately attempt to establish an instrumented portion of the deep sea capable of obtaining refined measurements of internal gravity waves.

Each set of measurements would be continued for long enough duration to contain roughly 100 of the longest period waves of interest. According to Eckart's analysis of internal gravity waves, we could anticipate that periods between 10 minutes and 1 day would be of primary interest, so that the duration of an individual set of measurements should be 100 days. This is a long time to keep a complicated array of many recording sensors operating at sea and would also lead to a formidable data-processing program. The array might consist of from 3 to 10 moored buoys with perhaps 10 to 20 vertically spaced sensors on each. The spacing horizontally between buoys would be varied: a working estimate to begin with could be 1 kilometer, the whole array being within a 4-minute square.

Measurements of horizontal velocity components recently made at Woods Hole Oceanographic Institution actually do not seem to indicate coherent wave motion. This may be an inherent difference in the nature of velocity and temperature structure in the ocean. Above tidal frequencies horizontal velocity components appear to consist of horizontally isotropic, incoherent eddies resembling turbulence. Horizontal scales range from 3 to 5 kilometers at the lower frequencies (0.1 cycle per hour) to perhaps 1 meter at the high-frequency limit of resolution of the current meters. Energy density decreases as the "minus 5/3" power of frequency. The motion is clearly not isotropic vertically and, because of vertical stratification, may have little vertical coherence. Vertical scales associated with this motion have not been determined.

As these turbulentlike fluctuations may be capable of developing a high vertical shear and perhaps generating shear turbulence, they may play a vital role in vertical mixing and transfer processes. Associated frequency distribution and spatial scales for temperature and salinity

113

are not known. The "minus 5/3" region contains frequencies that can be associated with internal waves. The particle velocities are sufficiently low that the waves cannot be identified in current measurements. However, they may be clearly identifiable in temperature fluctuations. Because considerable theoretical work has been carried out on internal waves, a concerted effort to measure both temperature and velocity may provide data necessary to test some theoretical deductions. At lower frequencies Fofonoff has found peaks in the kinetic-energy spectrum at semidiurnal tidal frequency and inertial frequency. Lesser peaks are found at 24 hours, at sum and difference frequencies of the inertial and tidal lines and at some higher harmonics of major peaks. The tidal line appears to vary to some extent, possibly because of the changing amplitude of tidal period internal waves. The inertial peak changes strongly with time and does not retain phase coherence. Inertial motion is usually, but not always, strongest near the surface and is observed at all depths. Neither the horizontal nor vertical scale is known. As in the higher frequency range, there is possibility of shear instability and generation of turbulence through phase incoherence with depth.

Energy density at inertial frequencies appears to be correlated with surface winds. At least in some records amplitude of inertial motion was found to be greater after passage of a storm. Present documentation is poor because of the lack of simultaneous measurements of both wind and surface currents.

Below inertial frequency energy density decreases to a minimum for periods of 2 to 5 days and then rises again at longer periods. Present records are insufficient to provide good resolution at these frequencies, and very little can be deduced from records collected to date except for the presence of large signals. Neither vertical nor horizontal scales are known, although buoys set several miles apart show strong coherence at periods greater than 5 days. The low-frequency region is accessible only through long-term measurement and is the basic motivation for establishing a continuing program of measurement at selected long-term sites.

3. ROSSBY-WAVE STUDY AS ANOTHER EXAMPLE: FOUR-DEGREE SQUARE

Another portion of the signal waveband to be monitored in oceans is associated with lower frequencies. To detect and measure these Rossby waves, it will be necessary to conduct a series of current measurements by buoys moored within a four-degree square for 4 successive years. Arrangement of buoys within the four-degree square is to be designed so that synoptic maps of irregular motions in oceans can be drawn, and relevant statistical properties of large-scale, long-period turbulent motions can be computed with an acceptable significance level.

In order to elucidate why it is crucial to obtain quantitative information on the transport of momentum and vorticity by large-scale eddy processes in oceans, we call attention to an analogous position in development of the theory of the atmosphere's general circulation about 10 years ago, when the fundamental quantitative studies of statistics of upper-air data carried out by Starr and his collaborators overthrew the classical picture of a predominantly meridional circulation, in which it was thought that the observed large-scale fluctuations played a more or less passive, dissipative role. Starr's investigations of observations demonstrated that fluctuations actually drive the mean circulation, and present-day theoretical studies of atmospheric circulation allow the fluctuations to play this more important role.

We are in a similar position in oceanography. The fundamental concept, about which all theoretical investigations from 1947 to 1962 are pivoted, is the basic Sverdrup relation between local curl of the mean wind stress and vertical integral of the meridional velocity component. The theory of the thermocline, thermohaline, and wind-driven circulation all depend upon this simple idea: That large-scale, quasi-geostrophic eddy processes do not play an important dynamical role in vorticity balance in the interior of the oceans.

During the past few years serious doubts about the neglecting of eddy processes have begun to arise:

(a) Aries measurements in the Atlantic, originally planned by Swallow, Crease, and Stommel to determine the mean velocity field at different depths, unexpectedly revealed the presence of large-scale, long-period eddies whose root mean square amplitudes were two orders of magnitude greater than the expected means, indeed so large that it is difficult to imagine that they can be decoupled from the mean fields as is implicit in the Sverdrup relation. At any rate irregular motions were so large that it was not possible to test the Sverdrup relationship in the simple way which the Aries measurements were originally intended to do. In order to obtain a statistical description of these eddy processes and to be able to map and describe them, it is evident that an effort at least an order of magnitude greater than the Aries measurements is necessary.

(b) Calculation of the amplitude of the abyssal circulation from IGY and Norpac data—by the method of Stommel (1956)—yields abyssal circulation rates much too large to be compatible with water-mass analysis and radiocarbon data. The same lack of agreement appears when the thermocline theory is semiquantitatively applied to actual density distribution in the ocean. These discrepancies also suggest that something important is omitted from the simple Sverdrup relation.

(c) Various simple theories of baroclinic instability (e.g. Phillips, 1951; Robinson, 1963), when applied to the laminar thermocline theories based on a laminor interior regime (following Sverdrup), indicate that the interior solution as given by the thermocline theories of Stommel, Robinson, and Welander is dynamically unstable. The immense complication connected with the theoretical problem of computing the fully developed geostrophic turbulent processes in the oceanic thermocline and the very incomplete observational description of such processes preclude further development of the unstable thermocline theory at present. When more observational guidelines are available, it seems probable that the theory can proceed, numerically if necessary. Of course, it is not at all clear whether the important property-transferring eddies owe their existence to instabilities of the thermocline or coastal boundary currents or to irregularities of bottom topography or applied wind stress.

(d) Early theories of oceanic circulation (Rossby, Hidaka, Stockmann) placed much emphasis on the hypothetical existence of large, lateral eddy transports. Sverdrup banished them from open oceans, and Munk found that their influence might be limited to the western sides of oceans and computed fields of transport in the oceans which bear considerable resemblance qualitatively to observed geographic mean distribution of ocean currents. The magnitude and role of eddy processes envisaged in the Munk theory is purely hypothetical.

One possible array is that 30 buoys be placed within a 4° square, centered at 32° N., 53° W. (an abyssal plain area). On each buoy there will be velocity and temperature measuring units at depths of 25, 50, 100, 200, 500, 1,000, 1,500, 2,000, 3,000, and 4,000 meters. Readings are taken at each point every 20 minutes for a year so that a total of 8×10^6 velocity vectors and 8×10^6 temperatures will be measured. Much of this information will be needed simply to filter out short-period components such as tides and their harmonics and short-period internal gravity wave phenomena.

4. OCEANWIDE NET AS AN EXAMPLE; QUARTER-OCEAN NET

Professor John Isaacs has proposed experiments with a much larger network of buoys—perhaps 80—covering a significant portion of the Pacific in order to monitor long-period changes in circulation. This type of network might be compatible with meteorological moored buoys of the World Weather Watch and might eventually be merged with that service.

5. HOW TO GET STARTED

Each of the three examples described above is a complicated expensive operation.

Such a program cannot spring into being overnight and must evolve from smaller pilot programs, but it is also evident that this evolution must be consciously planned in light of evolving understanding of the problems. Therefore, instead of proposing immediate organization of resources for undertaking a very large program of measurement, the immediate task as we see it is to set out a series of experiments in steps.

The following diagram indicates roughly how these might be scheduled.

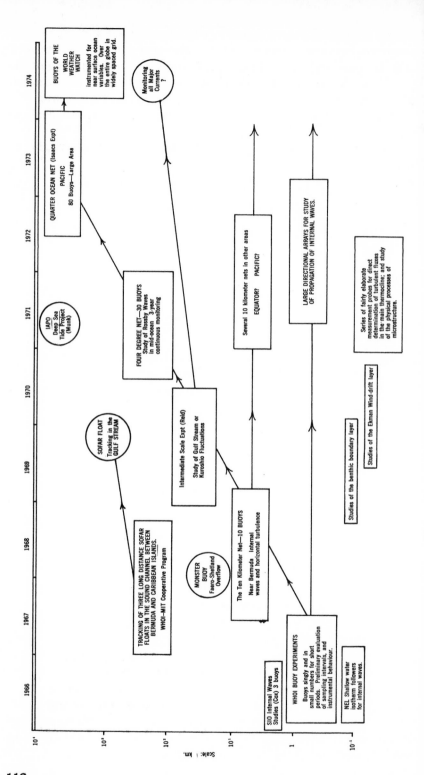

118

APPENDIX III

Industry and the Ocean Continental Shelf

1. INTRODUCTION

On September 20–23, 1965, a conference was held at the David Taylor Model Basin involving Government and industry to discuss their mutual roles in the exploration and exploitation of the Continental Shelf. The study was initiated by a letter from Dr. Robert W. Morse, Assistant Secretary of the Navy for Research and Development and chairman of the Interagency Committee on Oceanography, following a request from the PSAC Panel on Oceanography.

In order to assess the status of continental shelf development, it was decided to establish the following objectives:

a. Determine what industry is currently doing and what it intends to do concerning the exploration and exploitation of the Continental Shelf.

b. Determine oceanographic services currently available by the Federal Government and services desired by industry.

c. Elicit recommendations from industry concerning the desired mutual roles of industry and Government in the future exploitation of the Continental Shelf.

Five basic, nondefense industries were represented at the conference: petroleum, mining, chemical, fishing, and maritime industries. The Government was represented by the corresponding counterparts of the ICO. The attendees are listed below.

Since that time the study effort has continued within each panel, culminating in submission of individual panel reports in late 1965. Findings of each panel report are included in this appendix, and highlights of the recommendations are also listed. Several areas require more investigation before detailed recommendations can be made. Examples include undersea technology, undersea engineering standards, waste disposal, biological data handling, and the fishing industry in general. Accordingly, it is expected that follow-on studies will be made by pertinent panels in the near future.

119

2. RECOMMENDATIONS

It is recommended that the function of planning, correlating and carrying out of ocean research and use activities supported by the Federal Government be strengthened considerably. Additional recommendations are as follows:

a. *Prediction and Control of the Environment.* Inadequate prediction of weather, waves, and ocean climate has been responsible for inefficiency in operation, as well as serious loss of life and equipment to those who are engaged in offshore exploitation of resources. Therefore, it is recommended that:

1. Additional ocean weather stations for making measurements in mixed layers of the ocean and the atmosphere be constructed and installed.

2. More efficient use be made of data furnished by existing ocean weather stations in prediction programs.

3. Although modification/control of the environment still lies well in the future, steps toward its achievement should be taken now.

b. *Legal Problems.* Uncertainties and imperfections in Federal and State laws and leasing procedures deter potential undersea prospectors. This is in sharp contract, for example, to the situation existing on the Canadian Continental Shelf. Specifically, the Federal Government should do the following:

1. Establish and clarify its arrangements for ownership, leasing and royalty payments.

2. Clarify and minimize overlap in responsibilities of Federal agencies so that industry can readily determine which agency has primary responsibility for each area of interest, thereby simplifying procedures.

3. Distinguish clearly between State and Federal jurisdiction.

c. *Navigational Systems.* Accurate, reliable, and economical all-weather navigational systems are needed to permit industry to utilize existing charts and maps effectively and to perform its own mapping requirements. A company which has staked a claim in a given area must be able to relocate this area quickly, efficiently, and accurately. In this respect industry and government must work together in designing and manufacturing the best system. It is recommended that:

1. Navy navigational technology be made available to industry.

2. Classified information on this subject be made available as long as companies and individuals concerned meet proper security requirements.

d. *Surveys.* The Federal Government need not conduct detailed investigations from which industry traditionally develops its profit-oriented planning. Whereas the mining industry may want closer grid spacing to assist in the location of potential ore bodies, the oil industry would prefer broader spacing similar to the quality and degree of detail presently provided by the U.S. Geological Survey on land. It is recommended that:

1. Information obtained from presently planned surveys be disseminated in a timely and coordinated fashion; otherwise, its value will be limited.

2. The Federal Government conduct a survey of the U.S. continental shelf and the water column above, taking into consideration the broad experience of the U.S. Geological Survey.

e. *Information Services.* Industrialists are generally confused by the multiplicity of information services operated by the Federal Government. Accordingly, the following recommendations are made:

1. Information should be made available to industry by subject categories concerning who in the Government produces information, who stores it, the forms in which it may be retrieved, how it may be retrived, how it is categorized and subindexed, and the location of responsible Government contact points.

2. Classified information should be made available to industries having an established need.

Subsequent investigation of this subject area led to examination of several items in further detail. Thus, the present direction and funding of the National Oceanographic Data Center (NODC), which is by voluntary agreement of the participating agencies, does not adequately provide for sound management, planning, or growth to meet obvious needs. Second, although handling proprietary information from scientific and international political standpoints is now in effect at NODC, a doctrine for procedures in handling industrial data has yet to be worked out. Accordingly, the following recommendations are made:

1. The direction and funding responsibility of NODC should be placed under a single agency. Other agencies and customers should be served on a cost-reimbursable basis.

2. A doctrine for procedures in handling industrial data should be worked out through a joint task team study. OSTAC would be willing to work with the ICO on this matter.

3. The NODC should be exclusively responsible for storage, machine processing, retrieval, and dissemination of all marine physical, chemical, and bathymetric information and for such geological and biological information as lends itself to machine processing.

4. The Smithsonian Institution should continue to be responsible for the processing, storage, and distribution of all geological and biological specimens resulting from the national ocean program.

5. Finally, an additional recommendation concerning better exchange of information is that industry should provide an observer on the ICO on a rotating basis for a term of at least 1 year. OSTAC would be pleased to submit nominations, it being understood that the appointment would be subject to approval by ICO.

f. *Tax Writeoff.* A rational tax writeoff of funds invested in oceanographic exploration and exploitation would encourage and accelerate commercial exploitation of the Continental Shelf. The hostility of the shelf's environment and the lack of operating techniques make companies reluctant to invest. A wise tax law would encourage more commercial work in oceanography.

g. *Waste Disposal.* This is a subject requiring more investigation. However, as a start an appropriate Federal agency should establish reference points so that the effect of projected increases in the rate of disposal into the ocean can be accurately determined and a knowledge obtained as to the type of material being disposed.

h. *Oceanographic Instrumentations.* A National Oceanographic Instrumentation Center should be established under management and funding responsibility of a single agency. It should serve every agency on a cost-reimbursable basis. Its functions should include the service of calibration and standardization of instruments, development of standards and specifications, and consulting services on instrumentation development.

The above recommendations for single agency management of NODC and an NOIC do not contemplate duplication of present efforts. Furthermore, in each case the agency to be charged with the responsibility for the respective center should not only serve its own needs, but should be responsive to the interests of all Federal and State agencies, the scientific community, and industry.

3. PARTICIPANTS IN CONTINENTAL-SHELF CONFERENCE AT DAVID TAYLOR MODEL BASIN

Conference Planning Committee

ROBERT ABEL
Executive Secretary
Interagency Committee on Oceanography

JOHN H. JORGENSON
OSTAC Committee Executive
NSIA

AMOR L. LANE
Chairman, OSTAC Executive Committee
American Machine and Foundry Co.

Dr. THOMAS P. MELOY
Chairman, Continental Shelf Conference
Allis-Chalmers Manufacturing Co.

Capt. EDWARD SNYDER
Special Assistant to Assistant Secretary of the Navy (R. & D.)

Industry Panel Chairman and Coordinators

M. T. AQUINO
Merritt-Chapman & Scott Corp.
Maritime

DR. WILBERT M. CHAPMAN
Van Camp Sea Food Co.
Food-Fish

L. D. COATES
Lockheed-California Co.
Mining

ROGER W. FULLING
duPont de Nemours & Co.
Chemistry

DR. CHALMER G. KIRKBRIDE
Sun Oil Co.
(Presently Chairman, OSTAC)
Petroleum

Government Coordinators

JOSEPH M. CALDWELL
Corps of Engineers

DR. HARVE J. CARLSON
National Science Foundation

DR. JOHN P. CRAVEN
Bureau of Naval Weapons

COL. F. O. DIERKS
Corps of Engineers

HOWARD H. ECKLES
Department of the Interior

HARRY G. HANSON
Department of Health, Education, and
Welfare

MILTON JOHNSON
Department of Commerce

DR. EDWIN B. SHYKIND
Interagency Committee on Oceanography

Government Panel Members

*(In many cases those listed below appeared before more than one
industry panel)*

COL. C. W. BARBEE
U.S. Coast & Geodetic Survey

DR. GILBERT CORWIN
U.S. Geological Survey

H. W. DUBACH
National Oceanographic Data Center

LT. COMDR. CHARLES J. GLASS
U.S. Coast Guard Headquarters

G. R. GWINN
Bureau of Mines

THOMAS HICKLEY
U.S. Coast & Geodetic Survey

DR. FRED HUBBARD
Public Health Service

JOHN M. IDE
National Science Foundation

JAMES H. JOHNSON
Bureau of Commercial Fisheries

RICHARD L. KIRK
Atomic Energy Commission

FREDERICK KNOOP
Bureau of Yards and Docks

GORDON LILL
National Science Foundation

DR. JOHN LYMAN
Bureau of Commercial Fisheries

EDWARD M. MacCUTCHEON
Maritime Administration

MAX C. McLEAN
National Science Foundation

R. V. OCHINERO
National Oceanographic Data Center

FEODOR OSTAPOFF
Environmental Science Services Administration

N. E. PROMISEL
Bureau of Naval Weapons

STANLEY ROCKEFELLER
Bureau of Yards & Docks

DR. GEORGE J. ROTARIU
Atomic Energy Commission

PAUL ZINNER
Bureau of Mines

Industry Panel Members

Chemistry

ROGER W. FULLING
Chairman E. I. du Pont de Nemours
& Co.

J. C. BLAUVELT
American Cyanamid Co.

DR. JAMES H. GEORGE
A. D. Little, Inc.

J. A. SCHERER
Hercules Powder Co.

C. H. SHIGLEY
Dow Chemical Co.

FRED L. JOHNS
E. I. du Pont de Nemours & Co.

Food—Fish

DR. WILBERT M. CHAPMAN, *Chairman*
Van Camp Sea Food Co.

DR. H. W. BRUINS
Quaker Oats Co.

DR. B. F. BUCHANAN
General Foods Corp.

DR. I. J. HUTCHINGS
H. J. Heinz Co.

DR. C. T. SOLLENBERGER
Allis-Chalmers Co.

Maritime

M. T. AQUINO, *Chairman*
Merritt-Chapman & Scott Corp.

J. V. HARRINGTON
General Dynamics/Electric Boat

ADM. E. MORAN
Moran Towing & Transportation Co.

DANIEL T. MALLETT
George C. Sharp, Inc.

JOHN A. DAVIS, JR.
Grace Lines

CAPTAIN J. M. BALLINGER
Sun Shipbuilding & Drydock Co.

Mining

L. D. COATES, *Chairman*
Lockheed-California Co.

WILLARD BASCOM
Ocean Science & Engineering, Inc.

N. D. BIRRELL
Newport News Shipbuilding & Drydock Co.

F. E. BRIBER
Allis-Chalmers Manufacturing Co.

T. J. COLEMAN
Ocean Systems, Inc.

CHESTER O. ENSIGN
Copper Range Co.

PETER REISNER
International Minerals & Chemical Co.

PROF. ANTOINE GAUDIN
Massachusetts Institute of
Technology

THOMAS N. WALTHIER
Bear Creek Mining Co.

C. G. WELLING
Lockhead Missile & Space Co.

124

Petroleum

DR. CHALMER G. KIRKBRIDE, *Chairman*
Sun Oil Co.

F. GILMAN BLAKE
Chevron Research

DR. WARREN B. BROOKS
Socony Mobile Oil Co.

KEITH DOIG
Shell Oil Co.

HOLLIS D. HEDBERG
Gulf Oil Corp.

GEORGE C. HOWARD
Pan American Petroleum Co.

DR. RICHARD J. HOWE
Esso Production Research Co.

DR. MERTON E. SIMONS
Phillips Petroleum

DR. KARL C. tenBRINK
Texaco Corporation

DR. CHARLES L. THOMAs
Sun Oil Company

4. SUMMARY—FINDINGS OF THE FIVE INDUSTRIES

Industries involved in the study have different objectives and are in different states of technological involvement in the sea; as a result, they also have different problems. The significant findings are listed below.

Petroleum

a. The petroleum industry is committed to exploitation of the off-shore oil and gas fields.

b. It has an investment of over $10 billion and a recent annual sales rate of over $700 million.

c. The industry is increasing its own effort in research, development, and operations.

d. The technological problems of exploiting a commercial oil deposit in shallow to moderately deep water have been developed.

e. Its major concern is with finding an effective means of killing hurricanes in their early stages and improved services in environmental prediction.

f. The traditional guidelines established by the U.S. Geological Survey on land are believed to represent an appropriate separation of the government's and industry's proper spheres of action in the sea.

Mining

a. Sand and gravel constitute the largest single segment of the mining industry, totaling almost $900 million in 1964. About half of this came from coastal States, but only a small fraction was from offshore operations.

b. Sea-floor mining of sulfur and oyster shell resulted in about $45 million in sales in 1964.

c. Annual income derived from platinum dredging averaged about $1 million.

125

d. Negligible income is derived from known deposits of phosphorite, manganese nodules, gold, tin deposits, magnetite, chromite and titanium sands, calcium carbonate, and barite.

e. Techniques for underwater mining, except for dredging, have not been developed. The problem of exploiting a deposit of ore is more difficult by an order of magnitude than that required for oil.

f. The industry awaits the discovery of geologically promising areas.

Chemical

a. Six categories of this industry were considered. These include extraction of raw material, waste disposal, direct utilization of sea water (such as desalination), products of the chemical industry suitable for ocean environment, services of the chemical industry applicable to oceanography, and process development currently underway which has relevance to oceanography.

b. The interest of the chemical industry in further development of ocean resources is reflected in the relatively recent emergence of several ventures encompassing chemical industry firms and oceanographic-oriented enterprises.

c. The annual dollar volume of raw materials presently extracted from sea water is more than $200 million. The invested capital for sea and subsea minerals is estimated at over $300 million.

d. The chemical industry has a multitude of products which are required, in a hostile marine environment, for application and protection of personnel, manmade structures, equipment, fish, and plants. Current and projected ocean programs require new and improved products, including organic and inorganic chemicals, finishes, plastics, elastomers, metals, synthetic fibers, films, and photographic equipment.

e. Overall process engineering ability represents the biggest potential contribution the chemical industry can make.

Fishing

a. A large part of domestic fish production is made on, over, or in close relation to the Continental Shelf.

b. The fishing industry has a domestic capital investment in vessels, plants, etc., of about $1.4 billion. The value of the catch at the fisherman level in 1965 was $460 million. There is broad scope for increase.

c. Because of the common-property nature of fishery resources and conservation problems attendant thereto, the fishing industry relies almost exclusively on governmental and academic institutions for oceanographic research.

d. The industry is particularly interested in expansion of ocean research supported by the Government on the Continental Shelf regarding resource location and measurement, ocean-climate change and the effect of the latter on availability of resources.

e. The industry desires that better provision be made for dissemination of ocean science and technology findings to those that can use it, particularly to the fishermen.

Maritime

a. The panel considered the following in its study : coastal transport, ocean towage, ship and platform design, and salvage operations.

b. A recent report assessing the financial size of the industry shows an annual income of almost $2.5 billion for marine engineering (including shore protection, construction, harbor and channel construction maintenance, shipbuilding, and salvage). It also shows a rate of over $11 billion for transportation (including freight and passenger revenues and past income). In addition the industry is responsible for secondary outlays in the order of $8 billion. Hence, the total amount generated by the industry is about $22 billion a year.

c. The vital items of interest to the industry are related to its sociological aspects; i.e., its economics and labor relations.

d. Many areas of the industry are so busy trying to stay alive that little thought has been directed to oceanographic activities to be undertaken by the Government.

e. The industry is only now beginning to discover new uses for the technological base available to it and is making a start at substituting rational for traditional practices.

5. REFERENCES

References used by the five panels included, but were not limited to, the following:

a. "Ocean Engineering," Volumes I to VIII, edited by Richard D. Terry, North American Aviation, Inc., El Segundo, Calif., 1965.

b. Volume IV of Project SEABED report: "Advanced Sea-Based Deterrence, Summer Study 1964—Advanced Undersea Technology (U)," issued by the U.S. Naval Ordnance Laboratory, White Oak, Md., dated 8 March 1965.

c. Preliminary report, "An Economic Study of the Continental Shelf and U.S. Coast and Geodetic Survey Products and Services," prepared by the Battelle Memorial Institute for U.S. Department of Commerce, Coast and Geodetic Survey, August 18, 1965.

APPENDIX IV

The National Oceanographic Program—A Perspective [1]

The ocean has long had special significance to the people of the United States. Since colonial days we have both profited and suffered from our intimate relationship with the sea. Today, we face the sea along a general coastline of 12,500 miles. Our cities, villages, and farms have experienced the destructive forces of hurricanes and storm-generated waves. Our mariners have known the fury of troubled seas. Yet we have grown and prospered in many ways because of the sea. Quite early, our proximity to the ocean encouraged private enterprise to develop and expand industries such as fishing and shipbuilding. Opportunities for trade stimulated the growth of a merchant marine, which eventually projected U.S. maritime power throughout the world.

From the first days of the Republic, American industry looked to the Federal Government for protection and assistance in these endeavors. Thus, among its early acts, the Congress established in 1790 a seagoing Revenue Service (later the Coast Guard) to enforce U.S. laws at sea. In 1798, it authorized a navy, to defend our coasts and our ocean commerce, and a marine hospital service (later to become the Public Health Service) to provide medical care for merchant seamen. The Coast Survey (later the Coast and Geodetic Survey) was estabilshed in 1807 to improve navigation in coastal waters. As the Nation became more involved in the marine environment, the Federal Government assumed additional responsibilities in the national interest: To dredge harbors and navigable channels (U.S. Army Corps of Engineers, 1824); to protect and improve the management of our fishery resources (Department of State, 1828; and the U.S. Fish Commission, 1871—later, the Bureau of Commercial Fisheries and the Bureau of Sport Fisheries and Wildlife); to provide charting and

[1] Preface: National Oceanographic Program, fiscal year 1967, ICO Pamphlet No. 24, 1966.

routing services to naval and merchant ships (the Depot of Charts and Instruments—1830, now the Naval Oceanographic Office). In assuming these responsibilities, the Government sought practical solutions to practical problems, principally in the fields of navigation and fisheries.

In the 19th century, the scientific community emerged to give new direction to our efforts at sea. Here, as in Europe, naturalists with an interest in the marine environment were essentially landbound, working from small boats in shallow waters and along beaches. A few men, however, sought a broader understanding of the ocean's processes, boundaries, and contents. Their research required the collection of data over broad ocean areas, but only the Government was in a position to provide the facilities for such oceanwide studies. Throughout most of the century, the Navy, the Coast and Geodetic Survey, and the Smithsonian Institution (founded in 1846) encouraged scientists to accompany Government-sponsored expeditions. The Navy, through the efforts of Matthew Fontaine Maury, requested mariners to make systematic observations of winds and currents from merchant vessels so that forecasts could be made of sailing conditions in distant oceans.

Thus, research and data collection—insofar as it was relevant to an agency's mission—was encouraged and often supported by the Federal Government. By the early 1870's, for example, our New England fisheries clearly required a scientific basis for management. But few scientists were then available in Government to provide this support. Fortunately, the Smithsonian Institution—the only Government agency at that time with a charter permitting it to conduct basic research—was able to encourage naturalists to perform research for the U.S. Fish Commission. Spencer F. Baird, assistant secretary of the Smithsonian, became first Commissioner of Fish and Fisheries (1871).

By the turn of the century, working relationships with the scientific community—small as it then was—had been established by all agencies with ocean-oriented missions. Industry, too, had a stake in the modest but active programs of these agencies, especially the fishing and shipping interests. Furthermore, strong international ties had been established between marine scientists in the United States and Europe.

Following World War I, the Navy, the Coast Guard, the Fish Commission, and the Coast and Geodetic Survey continued their essentially descriptive work at sea. Nevertheless, there was concern on the part of the recently established National Research Council (NRC) of the National Academy of Sciences (NAS) that the marine sciences in the United States lacked sufficient scientific leadership. In contrast to Europe, where marine scientists enjoyed wide government support and recognition, the United States had few institutional facilities for training and developing leadership in oceanography. Recognizing this need, the National Research Council established its first Committee on Oceanography (NASCO), in 1927, to consider the role of the United States in a worldwide program of oceanographic research. The Committee report had a major impact upon the scientific community and was instrumental in obtaining—from philanthropic sources—funds for endowing institutions on both coasts and for constructing a ship and a few shore facilities.

During the 1930's, such oceanographic laboratories as the Scripps Institution of Oceanography and the Woods Hole Oceanographic Institution became the centers of scientific excellence which were to serve the United States so well during World War II. Then, for the first time, investigations were pressed by the Federal Government in an effort to apply oceanography to the solution of urgent defense problems. The small nucleus of oceanographers trained in the 1930's was augmented by scientists from other disciplines, many of whom remained associated with the marine sciences after the war.

Following World War II, oceanographic programs in the Office of Naval Research, the Navy Hydrographic Office (now the Naval Oceanographic Office), the Bureau of Ships, the Bureau of Commercial Fisheries, and the newly established Atomic Energy Commisison expanded to meet the growing problems of the marine environment. At the same time, the Government continued to support oceanographic research at universities and research institutions. By 1949, the National Academy of Sciences again became concerned over the relative growth of the marine sciences in the United States. A second Committee on Oceanography was appointed. Rather than urge a greatly expanded effort, the Academy's 1951 report stressed the necessity of regaining the balanced program of basic research that had characterized oceanography in the years before the war. Coming as it did in the first year of the Korean conflict, the report failed to stimulate effective action. However, in 1951, the National Science Foundation (NSF) made its first grant in the field of oceanography, and by 1954 a significant percentage of the grants in NSF's Environmental Biology and Earth Sciences programs had been made in oceanography.

A third NAS/NRC Committee on Oceanography was established in 1957. At that time the United States was spending less than $35 million annually for studies of the ocean out of a national basic research budget of well over $1 billion. Three Federal agencies with oceanographic programs (Atomic Energy Commission, Bureau of Commercial Fisheries, and the Office of Naval Research) requested the Committee to identify the national requirements for oceanographic research and to propose a 10-year program for their accomplishment. It was apparent from the Academy's deliberations that the traditional concept of "oceanography" as basic science had changed since the

1930's. While emphasizing oceanography as an interdisciplinary science, the NASCO panels addressed themselves to such subjects as marine resource development, ocean engineering, and man's effect upon the ocean environment—all very "practical" concerns directly related to the national interest. Programs that had never been recognized as "oceanography" in its classical sense were considered: Marine biology; water pollution control; shellfish sanitation; recreation; and coastal and deep ocean engineering. "Oceanography" had been broadened to include many aspects of man's activities in or on the ocean.

In considering the problems identified by its panels, the Academy was concerned, on the one hand, with an assessment of the needs of the field, and on the other, with such limitations on its development as the rate at which ships and facilities could be built and new manpower trained. The report concluded that: "Action on a scale appreciably less than that recommended will jeopardize the position of oceanography in the United States relative to the position of the sciences in other major nations, thereby accentuating serious military and political dangers, and placing the Nation at a disadvantage in the future use of the resources of the sea."

When released in 1959, the first chapters of the 12-volume report catalyzed action by both the executive and the legislative branches of Government. In the Senate, a resolution concurring in the NASCO recommendations passed unanimously. A subcommittee on Oceanography was established by the House Merchant Marine and Fisheries Committee. Legislation was enacted to strengthen the marine sciences by removing certain statutory limitations upon the Coast Guard, Coast and Geodetic Survey, and Geological Survey, enabling these agencies to participate in broader oceanographic work. In the executive branch, the recommendations were considered by the President's Science Advisory Committee (PSAC), which had earlier concluded that oceanography was a neglected field requiring additional emphasis. The PSAC endorsed the objectives of the report and commended it for action to the newly established Federal Council for Science and Technology.

At the Council's request, the President's Science Adviser established a Subcommittee on Oceanography in mid-1959, with representatives from the Departments of Defense, Interior, and Commerce, the Atomic Energy Commission, the National Science Foundation, and the Bureau of the Budget.

The Subcommmittee on Oceanography, in turn, examined ways by which an overall and integrated national program in oceanography might be initiated by the Federal Government. The Subcommittee's report recognized that "the resources of the sea are of interest to every major department and agency of the Government, and that the strengthening of the marine sciences poses one of the most difficult problems of coordination in the organization of science in Government." It concluded that "it is evident that procedures for formulating programs within the several agencies are well established but that there are deficiencies in coordination between agencies, in providing adequate funding, and in the mechanisms for carrying out a coordinated national program." Among its general recommendations were:

1. That as a national objective the Federal Government undertake a program for a substantial and orderly expansion of effort in the field of oceanography.

2. That this expansion of the national effort * * * be planned in general conformity with the NASCO recommendations as modified in the Subcommittee's report.

3. That full advantage be taken of existing Federal programs which can support training, education, and basic research in oceanography.

4. That professional oceanographers and interested scientific and research institutions take vigorous action to recruit scientists and organize educational programs.

5. That the national program in oceanographic research and surveys be planned and conducted taking maximum advantage of the mutual benefits to be derived from international cooperation.

The Subcommittee went on to make the following specific recommendations:

1. That a permanent interagency committee be established by the Federal Council to implement, coordinate, and review a national program in oceanography.

2. That the Federal agencies concerned develop 10-year plans for expansion of their existing programs in oceanography consistent with the national objective.

In late 1959 the Federal Council for Science and Technology accepted and endorsed the recommendations of the Subcommittee. Oceanography was recognized as an important field requiring additional emphasis in the national interest. The Interagency Committee on Oceanography (ICO) was established in February 1960 as a permanent committee, charged to provide the essential direction and coordination by preparing annually a National Oceanograpic Program, incorporating the Committee's judgment as to balance and emphasis in terms of both long-range scientific needs and requirements of Government agencies. Represented on the ICO were those Federal agencies with statutory responsibilities involving the marine environment, and observers from NASCO and the Bureau of the Budget.

Ten-year plans were prepared by each of the member agencies and synthesized into a long-range national oceanographic plan for the period 1963–72 ("Oceanography, The Ten Years Ahead," ICO Pamphlet No. 10). Approved by the President in 1963, this plan (1) addressed itself to oceanographic problems of national interest, and (2) outlined the goals toward which a national oceanographic program must be directed to meet national needs. In effect, the plan provides a means by which Federal, academic, and industrial members of the oceanographic community can look ahead together by providing a perspective in which they can see their various programs in relation to each other and to the national goals they support.

In developing its annual programs since 1964, ICO has been guided by, but not bound to, the long-range plan. The annual program is based on the recommendations and findings of seven special ICO panels * which reflect skills and competence found in the agencies and provide a means for expression of many points of view. In planning the program, panel members identify technical needs in various areas, devise programs and measures to meet these needs, identify desirable allocations of technical effort among the agencies, and suggest the assignment of technical leadership.

The Interagency Committee on Oceanography reviews these panel recommendations and findings to assure an appropriate division of technical effort among the agencies as well as a meaningful balance of oceanographic effort. It examines the adequacy of the overall program and the manpower base required for its implementation. Finally, it recommends policies to improve the quality and vigor of the national effort.

The Committee's recommended program is in turn reviewed by the staff and consultants of the Office of Science and Technology, which forwards its comments to the Federal Council for Science and Technology for final review and approval.

The recommended program is then integrated into the agency programs through normal agency channels. The agencies themselves retain responsibility for accepting or rejecting specific projects, for developing or conducting their own annual programs, and for defending them individually before Congress.

This process helps reduce competition for such resources as skilled manpower and funds and promotes their most effective use; encourages centralized planning and joint cooperative enterprises, promotes communication among key members of the oceanographic community; fosters a realistic and effective balance of effort among participating agencies and institutions, prevents needless duplication of work, and makes possible an orderly progression toward goals important to the national interest.

---

*Research, Ocean Engineering, Surveys, Instrumentation and Facilities, Ships, Manpower, International Programs.

Earlier Views on Federal Reorganization of the Environmental Sciences

In 1884 the National Academy of Sciences recommended to the Congress that it consider the formation of a Department of Science. A Joint Commission of the Senate and House of Representatives held hearings to "consider the present organizations of the Signal Service, Geological Survey, Coast and Geodetic Survey, and the Hydrographic Office of the Navy Department, with the view to secure greater efficiency and economy of administration." John W. Powell, Director of the Geological Survey, presented extensive testimony at these hearings [1] and expressed views remarkably similar to those derived independently by the Panel 82 years later.

Powell thoroughly documented the interactions and interdependences of the agencies which were concerned with the environmental sciences at that time. "* * * I have endeavored to fully set forth the relations which exist between the Coast and Geodetic Survey and the Geological Survey, and I think that I have shown that these relations are many, far-reaching, and fundamental. I have also shown, in a less perfect manner, that the relations existing between the Geological Survey and the National Museum and Fish Commission are in like manner many, far-reaching, and fundamental" (p. 173) ; "thus it is that the Geological Survey is profoundly interested in the general problems of meteorology and in the operations of the Signal Service, and that the Signal Service is profoundly interested in the operations of the Geological Survey" (p. 175) ; "the Signal Service and the Geological Survey should work for each other and with each other" (p. 175).

On the basis of these interactions and interdependencies, Powell recommended the formation of a single agency incorporating the Geological Survey, the Coast and Geodetic Survey, the Smithsonian

---

[1] On the Organization of Scientific Work of the General Government, Government Printing Office, Washington, 1885.

Institution, and the National Observatory. He recommended that the hydrographic work of the Coast Survey be transferred to the Navy Hydrographic Office and was "loath to volunteer any opinion" about the organization of the Signal Service. Put in modern terms this is a recommendation to combine the Geological Survey, Coast and Geodetic Survey, and Bureau of Commercial Fisheries (which since 1884 has moved from the Smithsonian to Commerce to Interior). In this respect the Panel is in complete agreement. However, we are not loath to include the Weather Bureau (which in 1884 was in the Signal Service of the Army) and the Coast Survey hydrographic work which was not so clearly related to the environmental sciences 82 years ago. We also include part of the work of the Bureau of Mines which did not exist at that time.

APPENDIX VI

An Act

To provide for a comprehensive, long-range, and coordinated national program in marine science, to establish a National Council on Marine Resources and Engineering Development, and a Commission on Marine Science, Engineering and Resources, and for other purposes.

Be it enacted by the Senate and House of Representatives of the United States of America in Congress assembled, That this Act may be cited as the "Marine Resources and Engineering Development Act of 1966".

DECLARATION OF POLICY AND OBJECTIVES

SEC. 2. (a) It is hereby declared to be the policy of the United States to develop, encourage, and maintain a coordinated, comprehensive, and long-range national program in marine science for the benefit of mankind to assist in protection of health and property, enhancement of commerce, transportation, and national security, rehabilitation of our commercial fisheries, and increased utilization of these and other resources.

(b) The marine science activities of the United States should be conducted so as to contribute to the following objectives:

(1) The accelerated development of the resources of the marine environment.

(2) The expansion of human knowledge of the marine environment.

(3) The encouragement of private investment enterprise in exploration, technological development, marine commerce, and economic utilization of the resources of the marine environment.

(4) The preservation of the role of the United States as a leader in marine science and resource development.

(5) The advancement of education and training in marine science.

(6) The development and improvement of the capabilities, performance, use, and efficiency of vehicles, equipment, and instruments for use in exploration, research, surveys, the recovery of resources, and the transmission of energy in the marine environment.

(7) The effective utilization of the scientific and engineering

resources of the Nation, with close cooperation among all interested agencies, public and private, in order to avoid unnecessary duplication of effort, facilities, and equipment, or waste.

(8) The cooperation by the United States with other nations and groups of nations and international organizations in marine science activities when such cooperation is in the national interest.

THE NATIONAL COUNCIL ON MARINE RESOURCES AND ENGINEERING DEVELOPMENT

SEC. 3. (a) There is hereby established, in the Executive Office of the President, the National Council on Marine Resources and Engineering Development (hereinafter called the "Council") which shall be composed of—

(1) The Vice President, who shall be Chairman of the Council.
(2) The Secretary of State.
(3) The Secretary of the Navy.
(4) The Secretary of the Interior.
(5) The Secretary of Commerce.
(6) The Chairman of the Atomic Energy Commission.
(7) The Director of the National Science Foundation.
(8) The Secretary of Health, Education, and Welfare.
(9) The Secretary of the Treasury.

(b) The President may name to the Council such other officers and officials as he deems advisable.

(c) The President shall from time to time designate one of the members of the Council to preside over meetings of the Council during the absence, disability, or unavailability of the Chairman.

(d) Each member of the Council, except those designated pursuant to subsection (b), may designate any officer of his department or agency appointed with the advice and consent of the Senate to serve on the Council as his alternate in his unavoidable absence.

(e) The Council may employ a staff to be headed by a civilian executive secretary who shall be appointed by the President and shall receive compensation at a rate established by the President at not to exceed that of level II of the Federal Executive Salary Schedule. The executive secretary, subject to the direction of the Council, is authorized to appoint and fix the compensation of such personnel, including not more than seven persons who may be appointed without regard to civil service laws or the Classification Act of 1949 and compensated at not to exceed the highest rate of grade 18 of the General Schedule of the Classification Act of 1949, as amended, as may be necessary to perform such duties as may be prescribed by the President.

(f) The provisions of this Act with respect to the Council shall expire one hundred and twenty days after the submission of the final report of the Commission pursuant to section 5(h).

SEC. 4 (a) In conformity with the provisions of section 2 of this Act, it shall be the duty of the President with the advice and assistance of the Council to—

(1) survey all significant marine science activities, including the policies, plans, programs, and accomplishments of all departments and agencies of the United States engaged in such activities;

(2) develop a comprehensive program of marine science activities including, but not limited to, exploration, description and prediction of the marine environment, exploitation and conservation of the resources of the marine environment, marine engineering, studies of air-sea interaction, transmission of energy, and communications, to be conducted by departments and agencies of the United States, independently or in cooperation with such non-Federal organizations as States, institutions and industry;

(3) designate and fix responsibility for the conduct of the foregoing marine science activities by departments and agencies of the United States;

(4) insure cooperation and resolve differences arising among departments and agencies of the United States with respect to marine science activities under this Act, including differences as to whether a particular project is a marine science activity;

(5) undertake a comprehensive study, by contract or otherwise, of the legal problems arising out of the management, use, development, recovery, and control of the resources of the marine environment;

(6) establish long-range studies of the potential benefits to the United States economy, security, health, and welfare to be gained from marine resources, engineering, and science, and the costs involved in obtaining such benefits; and

(7) review annually all marine science activities conducted by departments and agencies of the United States in light of the policies, plans, programs, and priorities developed pursuant to this Act.

(b) In the planning and conduct of a coordinated Federal program the President and the Council shall utilize such staff, interagency, and non-Government advisory arrangements as they may find necessary and appropriate and shall consult with departments and agencies concerned with marine science activities and solicit the views of non-Federal organizations and individuals with capabilities in marine sciences.

SEC. 5. (a) The President shall establish a Commission on Marine Science, Engineering, and Resources (in this Act referred to as the "Commission"). The Commission shall be composed of fifteen members appointed by the President, including individuals drawn from Federal and State governments, industry, universities, laboratories and other institutions engaged in marine scientific or technological pursuits, but not more than five members shall be from the Federal Government. In addition the Commission shall have four advisory members appointed by the President from among the Members of the Senate and the House of Representatives. Such advisory members shall not participate, except in an advisory capacity, in the formulation of the findings and recommendations of the Commission. The President shall select a Chairman and Vice Chairman from among such fifteen members. The Vice Chairman shall act as Chairman in the latter's absence.

(b) The Commission shall make a comprehensive investigation and study of all aspects of marine science in order to recommend an overall plan for an adequate national oceanographic program that will meet the present and future national needs. The Commission shall undertake a review of existing and planned marine science activities of the United States in order to assess their adequacy in meeting the objectives set forth under section 2(b), including but not limited to the following:

(1) Review the known and contemplated needs for natural resources from the marine environment to maintain our expanding national economy.

(2) Review the surveys, applied research programs, and ocean engineering projects required to obtain the needed resources from the marine environment.

(3) Review the existing national research programs to insure realistic and adequate support for basic oceanographic research that will enhance human welfare and scientific knowledge.

(4) Review the existing oceanographic and ocean engineering programs, including education and technical training, to determine which programs are required to advance our national oceanographic competence and stature and which are not adequately supported.

(5) Analyze the findings of the above reviews, including the economic factors involved, and recommend an adequate national marine science program that will meet the present and future national needs without unnecessary duplication of effort.

(6) Recommend a Governmental organizational plan with estimated cost.

(c) Members of the Commission appointed from outside the Government shall each receive $100 per diem when engaged in the actual performance of duties of the Commission and reimbursement of travel expenses, including per diem in lieu of subsistence, as authorized in section 5 of the Administrative Expenses Act of 1946, as amended (5 U.S.C. 73b–2), for persons employed intermittently. Members of the Commission appointed from within the Government shall serve without additional compensation to that received for their services to the Government but shall be reimbursed for travel expenses, including per diem in lieu of subsistence, as authorized in the Act of June 9, 1949, as amended (5 U.S.C. 835–842).

(d) The Commission shall appoint and fix the compensation of such personnel as it deems advisible in accordance with the civil service laws and the Classification Act of 1949, as amended. In addition, the Commission may secure temporary and intermittent services to the same extent as is authorized for the departments by section 15 of the Administrative Expenses Act of 1946 (60 Stat. 810) but at rates not to exceed $100 per diem for individuals.

(e) The Chairman of the Commission shall be responsible for (1) the assignment of duties and responsibilities among such personnel and their continuing supervision, and (2) the use and expenditures of funds available to the Commission. In carrying out the provisions of this subsection, the Chairman shall be governed by the general policies of the Commission with respect to the work to be accomplished by it and the timing thereof.

(f) Financial and administrative services (including those related to budgeting, accounting, financial reporting, personnel, and procurement) may be provided the Commission by the General Services Administration, for which payment shall be made in advance, or by reimbursement from funds of the Commission in such amounts as may be agreed upon by the Chairman of the Commission and the Administrator of General Services: *Provided,* That the regulations of the General Services Administration for the collection of indebtedness of personnel resulting from erroneous payments (5 U.S.C. 46d) shall apply to the collection of erroneous payments made to or on behalf of a Commission employee, and regulations of said Administrator for the administrative control of funds (31 U.S.C. 665(g)) shall apply to appropriations of the Commission: *And provided further,* That the Commission shall not be required to prescribe such regulations.

(g) The Commission is authorized to secure directly from any executive department, agency, or independent instrumentality of the Government any information it deems necessary to carry out its functions under this Act; and each such department, agency, and instrumentality is authorized to cooperate with the Commission and, to the extent permitted by law, to furnish such information to the Commission, upon request made by the Chairman.

(h) The Commission shall submit to the President, via the Council, and to the Congress not later than eighteen months after the establishment of the Commission as provided in subsection (a) of this section, a final report of its findings and recommendations. The Commission shall cease to exist thirty days after it has submitted its final report.

INTERNATIONAL COOPERATION

SEC. 6. The Council, under the foreign policy guidance of the President and as he may request, shall coordinate a program of international cooperation in work done pursuant to this Act, pursuant to agreements made by the President with the advice and consent of the Senate.

REPORTS

SEC. 7 (a) The President shall transmit to the Congress in January of each year a report, which shall include (1) a comprehensive description of the activities and the accomplishment of all agencies and departments of the United States in the field of marine science during the preceding fiscal year, and (2) an evaluation of such activities and accomplishments in terms of the objectives set forth pursuant to this Act.

(b) Reports made under this section shall contain such recommendations for legislation as the President may consider necessary or desirable for the attainment of the objectives of this Act, and shall contain an estimate of funding requirements of each agency and department of the United States for marine science activities during the succeeding fiscal year.

DEFINITIONS

SEC. 8. For the purposes of this Act the term "marine science" shall be deemed to apply to oceanographic and scientific endeavors and disciplines, and engineering and technology in and with relation to the marine environment; and the term "marine environment" shall be deemed to include (a) the oceans, (b) the Continental Shelf of the United States, (c) the Great Lakes, (d) seabed and subsoil of the submarine areas adjacent to the coasts of the United States to the depth of two hundred meters, or beyond that limit, to where the depths of the superjacent waters admit of the exploitation of the natural resources of such areas, (e) the seabed and subsoil of similar submarine areas adjacent to the coasts of islands which comprise United States territory, and (f) the resources thereof.

AUTHORIZATION

SEC. 9. There are hereby authorized to be appropriated such sums as may be necessary to carry out this Act, but sums appropriated for any one fiscal year shall not exceed $1,500,000.

Subject Index

Abyssal ocean : 46

Air-sea boundary : 47

Anchovy : 7, 9

Antarctic program : 86

Antisubmarine Warfare : 30, 103

Aquiculture : Ch. 2.0, 78

Arctic ice : 43

Arctic marine laboratory : 100

Arctic program : 86

ARPA : 84

Atmosphere : XVI, 41

Atomic Energy Commission : XVI, 86

Benthic boundary : XIV, 91, 92, 102

Biomedical problems : XI, XIII, 37, 52, 54

Biotoxins : 53

Bottom-mounted installations : 93

Buoys : XIV, 26, 46, 47, 94, 98, 103, 112, 113

Bureau of Commercial Fisheries : XV, 10, 12, 63, 84, 88, 89, 128, 130, 135

Bureau of Mines : 84, 88, 89

Bureau of Sport Fisheries and Wildlife : 84, 128

Bureau of the Budget : XVI, 90

Chemical industry : 119, 126

Clams : 11

Classification policy : 35

Coastal boundary : 48

Coastal Engineering Research Center : 25, 84, 103

Coast and Geodetic Survey : 85, 135

Coast Guard : XV, 85, 88, 89, 97

Codfish : 18

Commerce, Department of : 85

Congress : IX, XVI, 18, 40, 61, 80, 84, 90

Continental Shelf : 92, 93, 94

Corps of Engineers : 59, 84

Data processing : 41, 42

Deep-ocean tide : 45

Deep-sea instrumentation : 98

Deep Submergence Systems : XI, 36, 37, 39, 40, 68, 83, 102

Defense, Department of : 83

Desalinization : 16, 17

Diamonds : 28

Earthquakes : 43

Education in oceanography : 76, 104

Eltanin : 95

Environmental prediction : 57

Environmental sciences : XIII, XVI, 1, 41, 89

Environmental Science Services Administration : XV, 35, 40, 85, 88

Federal Council for Science and Technology : XVI, 67, 81, 86, 90

Federal Government, role : X

Federal Water Pollution Control Administration : 85

Fisheries : 60, 74, 92

Fishing industry : 119, 126

Fleets : 96, 97

Food chains : 50

Fuel-cell power systems : 102

"General circulation" : 46

Geological Survey : XV, 84, 88, 89, 121, 125, 135

Geophysical fluid dynamics : 48

Gold : 28, 126

Great Lakes : 17

Great Society Programs : 61, 105

Gulf Stream : 43

Hake : 9, 10

Health, Education, and Welfare : XVI, 85, 90

Hydrodynamics : 44

Hydrographic Survey Program : 35, 103

Interior, Department of the : 84

Interagency Committee on Atmospheric Sciences : XVI, 90

Interagency Committee on Oceanography, role of : 86

Interagency Committee on Oceanography : XVI, 4, 66, 67, 68, 71, 72, 81, 82, 83, 86, 90, 106, 119, 121, 132, 133

Intergovernmental Oceanographic Commission : 67

"Internal waves" : 112, 113

Internal tides: 113

International Council of Scientific Unions: 67

International Geophysical Year: 67, 80

International Indian Ocean Expedition: 67

Iron ores: 28

JOIDES: 45, 48, 84

Legal problems: 91, 120

Legislation: IX, 80

Magnetic Anomaly Detection (MAD): 31

Magnetite: 126

Manganese nodules: 126

Man in the Sea: XI, 27, 39, 99

Marine food resources: XII, 2, 50, 92

Marine mining: 78

Marine organisms, supply of: 52, 100

Marine populations: 49, 51

Marine Resources and Engineering Development Act of 1966: 136

Marine Study Center: XIV, 79, 91

Marine wilderness: XIII, 18

Maritime Administration: 85

Maritime industry: 119, 127

Mining industry: 119, 125

Mineral resources: 28

Modification of environment: 1, Ch. 3, 43, 57, 120

MOHOLE: 22, 45, 48, 68, 86, 95

Moored-buoy arrays: APP. II

Municipal government: 73

NASCO Report on Economic Benefit From Oceanography Research: 57, 58, 59, 60

National Academy of Sciences: 4, 66, 80, 130

National Aeronautics and Space Administration: 86

National Fishery Center and Aquarium: 101

National goals: X, 1

National Institutes of Health: 85

National Oceanographic Data Center: 88, 97, 98, 121

National Oceanography Instrumentation Center: 122

National Science Foundation: XVI, 56, 57, 63, 68, 71, 72, 78, 84, 86, 87, 89, 90, 96

National security: X, Ch. 5, 102

Navy Hydrographic Office: 130, 134, 135

Naval Oceanographic Office: 83, 130

Navigation: 21, 61, 120

Navy: X–XVII, Chs. 1, 4, 5, 6, 10, 11

Navy's Oceanographic Program: 34

Navy's role in Education and Research: 37

Near-shore environment: XIII, 61, 103

Nuclear-powered oceanographic vehicle (NR–1): 36

Nuclear weapons, recovery: XI, XII, Ch. 5

Oceanic circulation: 41, 116

Oceanographers, number of: 70, 71

Oceanography, defined: IX

Ocean resources: XVI, 2

Ocean weather: 43, 49, 103

Ocean weather stations: 120

Office of Education: 85

Office of Naval Research: XII, XVI, 37, 39, 68, 78, 83, 87, 90, 102

Oysters: 11, 12, 13, 125

Oyster culture, Japanese: 13

Panel membership: APP. I

Panel objectives: IX

Peru: 7

Petroleum industry: 74, 119, 125

Phosphorite: 28, 126

Phytoplankton: 7, 11, 13, 14, 49, 50

Polaris: 32, 33

Pollution: XIII, 17, 57, 61, 78

Poseidon: 33

Power plants: 26, 102

Prediction of environment: X, XI, 89, 103, 120

Protein: XII, Ch. 2.0

Public Health Service: 12, 85, 128

Radioactive wastes: 17

Raw materials: 59, 60, 94

Reactor technology: 26

Resources: X, 28

Rossby wave: 112, 114

Royalties, petroleum industry: 74

Science, Department of: 81, 134

Scripps Institution of Oceanography: 68, 95

Sea-air interaction laboratory: 87

Sea-bottom conditions: 89

Sea-level canal: XIII, 16, 17, 51

Search and recovery missions: XI, 34, 36

Shellfish: 11, 12

Ships: XV, XVII, 95

Ship funding: 95

Ship operations : XV, 95
Shrimp : 11, 14
Smithsonian Institution : XVI, 86, 90, 121, 129
Sonar : 31, 45
Soviet submarine force : 30
Squid : 14, 52
Standards : 24
State, Department of : 85, 128
State government : 73
State laws : 120
Surface waves : 43, 47
Surveys : XIV, 23, 41, 54, 120
Survey technology : 103
"Swallow" floats : 41
Temperature Zone Marine Laboratory 100
Test range : XII, 39
Thermocline : 46, 115, 116
Thermohaline circulation : 115
Thresher : XI, 34, 36, 38, 40
Tidal friction : 45

Tidal predictions : 42
Tides : 42
Tin : 28, 126
Titanium : 126
Tools : 21, 22
Treasury, Department of : 85
Tropical Marine Laboratory : 100
Tsunamis : 43
Undersea technology : XI, XIV, 119
User groups : 96, 97
Waste heat : 17
Wave generation : 43, 48
Weather Bureau : 57, 85, 135
Weather in oceans : XIV
Weather modification : 16, 18, 19
Whales : 17
Wilderness Act : 18
Wind-driven circulation : 115
Woods Hole Oceanographic Institution : 68, 95
World Weather Watch : 26
Zooplankton : 7, 14

54

☆U.S. GOVERNMENT PRINTING OFFICE : 1970 O - 402-280

71 182 S   P 70 3

DUQUESNE UNIVERSITY LIBRARY
PITTSBURGH, PA. 15219

DATE DUE

3 5282 00300 4473